SONS OF THE VOLSUNGS

THE MACMILLAN COMPANY
NEW YORK · BOSTON · CHICAGO
DALLAS · ATLANTA · SAN FRANCISCO

MACMILLAN AND CO., LIMITED
LONDON · BOMBAY · CALCUTTA
MADRAS · MELBOURNE

THE MACMILLAN COMPANY
OF CANADA, LIMITED
TORONTO

Sigurd and Greyfell.

"The Name of the Volsungs must not perish."

SONS
OF THE
VOLSUNGS

Adapted by DOROTHY G. HOSFORD
from SIGURD THE VOLSUNG
by WILLIAM MORRIS

Illustrated by Frank Dobias

THE MACMILLAN COMPANY
NEW YORK   1943

PRINTED IN THE UNITED STATES OF AMERICA
AMERICAN BOOK—STRATFORD PRESS, INC., NEW YORK

To Raymond

CONTENTS

[ix]

CONTENTS

[x]

LIST OF ILLUSTRATIONS

Of the dwelling of King Volsung, and
the wedding of Signy his daughter, and
of her departure for the land of the Goths

In the days when the world was young, in the land of the
North, there lived a king, Volsung by name. The roofs of his
dwelling were thatched with gold; the great doors were barred
with silver. The men of his court were earls famed for their
prowess in battle, and dukes whose ships had sailed the far seas.
He ruled over a noble and merry-hearted people, who met bravely
the good days and the evil that life sent them. And as the land
of Volsung was known throughout the world for its strength
and its greatness, it was known also for a marvelous thing. In the
center of the great hall where Volsung held his court, there
sprang up a mighty tree. Its leafy boughs spread above the hall;
its great height rose even beyond the crest of the roof. Wild
hawks flew in and out among its branches and nested there.
At the feasts the sound of their wailing could be heard amid
the laughter and the songs. I do not know what, in the beginning of time, the tree was called. But in the many tales that are

[1]

told of the deeds of Volsung, of his battles and his fame, it is named the Branstock.

So the tree stood on an evening in May, and Volsung and his people were gathered beneath it, when there appeared a messenger from Siggeir, King of the Goths. He spake his message to Volsung:

"All hail to thee, King Volsung, from the King of the Goths I come. My king hath heard of thy victories in battle and of thy fair land. He hath heard of the deeds of thy warlike sons and he hath heard, moreover, of the great beauty of thy daughter Signy. He deems thy friendship goodly and thy help in battle good, and for these will he give again his friendship and his aid. But if thou wouldst grant his request and fill his heart with gratitude, thou wouldst grant him that which is beyond any price but which he desireth beyond all things, the hand of Signy, the fairer than fair, Signy, the wiser than wise."

These words spake the messenger of the King of the Goths, bearing with him gifts of gold and precious gems, and the ring with which to plight the betrothal. King Volsung heard the words of the messenger with joy, for he knew that the King of the Goths was a powerful king and that their two houses joined together might accomplish many things. But he said nought until he had turned to Signy beside him: "A great king woos thee, daughter. Wilt thou become his wife and bring to our name and our land new honor?"

Signy answered him, and in her eyes there was a strange light and her voice was sharp as a cry: "I will become the wife of a king and the mother of kings. And all the grief and the beauty of my youth shall come to nought."

These were strange words and Signy looked strangely, and Volsung questioned his daughter to know what her meaning might be. But she answered: "Would that my life might be otherwise. But what is to be must be. For whatever thou might say, I should will to marry the King of the Goths, though I know what the years may hold. So is it written."

Signy said these words softly, but now she spake more loudly: "Be of good cheer, my father. All things that you do knowingly are brave and good. What you do without knowing the Gods have bidden you to do. And in the end all things will work together for the fame of thee and thine. And I seem to know that at my wedding something will happen which will be a token and a sign that will give you happiness, whatever may come after." So the feast went on, and in the singing of songs and the laughter, the sorrow of Signy's words were forgotten.

On the morrow the earl of the King of Gothland returned again home, bearing with him gifts and gold from Volsung. He took with him, too, the joyful message to his king that the hand of Signy the Fair should be his.

So it came to pass that in the midsummer, Siggeir, the King

[3]

of the Goths, came with many of his earls to the court of Volsung to claim his bride. They were splendid in their bearing, King Siggeir and his earls: the woods rang out with the sound of their armor, their garments were marvelously fashioned, their hands were adorned with curiously wrought jewels. Yet, as they came forward to receive the greeting of King Volsung who awaited them, with his sons on either hand, they were as small men in comparison. Beside Volsung, Siggeir the Goth was as a small bramble tree beside a mighty oak, and he reached not to the shoulder of the least of Volsung's sons. With friendliness they greeted one another and wended their way into the mighty hall to the feast which was prepared for them. The feast lasted throughout the night, almost to the break of day. Only for a few hours in the early morning did they sleep, and a summer rain fell quietly.

The next day the feast was even more glorious, and now Signy sat beside King Siggeir as his bride. Truly she deserved the name of Signy the Fair, for she was lovely, but now she neither laughed nor spake and her eyes were hard and cold as she watched, with sidelong looks, Siggeir, her lord. Sigmund, her brother, the eldest son of Volsung, saw this and often and again he looked at his sister, and their glances met. Hate and anger rose in the heart of Sigmund against Siggeir the Goth and thereupon would he have broken the wedding, but that the promise had been made. Siggeir beheld the glance that passed between

Sigmund and his sister, and he deemed that here he should win little glory, but he spake nothing, nor gave any hint of that which he thought, waiting only the time that was to come, and joining now, with the loudest, in the laughter and the merriment. None of all this saw Volsung, thinking only of the greatness of his race in the days that were to be.

So round the Branstock, that great tree of which I told you, the feast went on merrily. And though the days of the world were yet young, they had tales of the deeds of men and of the beginning of all things. From among them arose a sea king, and with the strong hands that mastered the oars, he touched the strings of his harp. He sang of the shaping of earth, and how the stars were lighted, and where the winds had birth.

But even as men's hearts were listening to his tale, some thought they heard the thunder pass over the clear noontide heaven and others thought that in the doorway they heard a man laugh out. Then into the Volsung dwelling there strode a mighty man. He had but one eye and seemed an ancient man, but about his head there was a strange brightness and beauty. His hood was of cloud blue and his kirtle of gleaming grey, and on his shoulder he bore a bill which shone as though the shining spray of the ocean and the gleam of silver had been caught within it. The elders of Volsung's court knew that the raiment of the one-eyed and seeming ancient man was that worn by their fathers' fathers, in the earliest days of the world. He strode to

[5]

the Branstock, nor spake a word. Then, forth from his cloudy raiment he drew a gleaming sword and smote it deep into the tree trunk. Overhead the wild hawks laughed out and circled in its branches. Then turned he to the company and spake:

"Earls of the Goths, and Volsungs, abiders on the earth: Lo, there amid the Branstock lies a keen and valiant sword. Ne'er, since the first days of the world, has blade been forged of finer steel. Let the man among you now who is strongest in heart and hand pluck it from the oakwood, and for him shall it be my gift. Then ne'er, but his own heart falter, shall it fail him in his need. And now I bid you farewell, but for only a little while. For I have heard of a mighty battle which shall claim the great ones of the earth and soon shall many brave ones come to the wide and shining house of heaven. And there shall they find abundant rest and on earth shall men no more know their like. So, Earls of the Goths, and Volsungs, I bid you now farewell."

His words sounded so sweet and so wise in the saying that as he spake men sat without moving as though fearful to disturb a happy dream. He ended his words and slowly made his way out of the hall. None questioned him nor followed him from the door, for they knew that the gift was Odin's, and in their hearts they trembled a little.

But now King Volsung spake: "Why do ye sit silent and still? Do ye fear the token of the Battle Father? Arise, O Volsung children; Earls of the Goths, arise! Set your hands upon the hilt! But think ye not that 'twill be easy, for belike 'tis a fateful blade that lies there deep in the Branstock, and 'twill come loose for none but him who is Odin's choice."

Then up spake King Siggeir: "King Volsung, I ask of you the right to try it first of all men, lest another win before me and mere chance steal my glory and my gain."

King Volsung laughed somewhat, but he answered: "O Guest, begin; though herein is the first as the last, for Odin hath not forgotten unto whom he would give the gift."

Then Siggeir, the mighty lord of the Goth folk, went forth to the tree. He caught hold of the jeweled hilt of the sword, and again and again strained to lift it from its place, till his heart grew black with anger. Not a word spake he as he wended his way back to the high-seat, but Signy, as he sat himself beside her, felt her face grow red with shame and with foreboding.

Then spake King Volsung: "And thus comes back empty-handed the mightiest king of earth? How shall the feeble venture? Yet each man knows his worth. And today, mayhap, will mark the beginning of a new name and new deeds that will arise to o'erpass many a one who hath now the name of king. So stand forth free and unfree; stand forth both most and least. But first, ye Earls of the Goth folk, ye lovely lords we feast."

The earls of Siggeir stood forth. Each man took his turn at the sword with the hope in his heart that he might win glory and high gain, but for all their mighty effort and their battle strength, the gift of Odin moved not an inch from its resting place. Then stood forth Volsung's homemen: the dwellers in the forest, the yellow-headed shepherds, the hunters and the sailors, and even the least of them was a mighty man of war. But for all their mighty effort and the skill and strength of their hands, in vain they tugged at the sword. Those gathered about shouted their encouragement or their jeers, and the words and the laughter echoed back from gable to gable. But on his high-seat Siggeir sat moody and silent, and he brooded to himself: "They have trapped me here as a mock for their woodland bondsmen, but yet shall they buy their pleasure dear."

The tumult sank a little and men cried on King Volsung and his sons, they who were the very front of the battle, to try the fateful thing. So Volsung laughed and answered:

"I, too, will try the sword, lest my guests, the Goth folk, should deem I fear the foil. But the sword that I bear is a brave one and has served me long and well. The oldest friend is best. Ne'er shall I wield another sword; yea, even in the Day of Doom when I stand in the midst of the host of Odin shall this be in my hand."

And from his battle belt he held aloft the golden sheath and showed the glittering peace-strings wrapped about it. Then he laid his hand on the Branstock and cried:

"O tree beloved, I thank thee of thy good heart that so little

[8]

thou art moved. Abide thou thus, green bower, when I am dead and the best of all my kindred hath won a better day."

So speaking, he laughed as a young man and laid hold of the shining hilt of the Sword of Odin. And long he drew and strained him, but loosened not the sword. But the mirth of his heart did not fail him. Wending his way back to his high-seat he spake:

"Sons I have gotten and cherished, now stand ye forth to try, lest Odin tell in the God-home that to a man who hath not deserved it, he hath given away his blade."

Then the sons of Volsung stepped forth. First Rerir tried his might, then Gunthiof and then Hunthiof, but their efforts availed nought; neither Agnar, nor Helgi, nor Sigi the tall, could move the sword. Then Solar, and Geirmund, who was priest of the temple, and Gylfi, all put forth their strength; but the glittering sword stood firm in the Branstock.

At last Sigmund the Volsung stood forth and with his right hand, so wise in battle, took hold of the precious hilt of the sword. But he laid his hand lightly on it as though knowing that he too should avail nothing. When lo, a mighty shout went up, a shout that rebounded against the very rafters and startled the hawks in their flying, for aloft in the hand of Sigmund the naked blade shone out. As though it had lain all loose in the heart of the Branstock, the sword had come forth in his hand. For a moment he stood in the midst of the great hall, stalwart and silent, like the best of the trees in the garden. Then soberly he wended back to the high-seat, for this was the thought within him:

"Belike the day will come when I alone shall bide here, the last in this Volsung home. Yea, the day may come when I only shall be left of all the Volsungs, their glory and sole avenger. Truly am I hired of Odin and I must work his will, and the way will not be easy. It were well, mayhap, if all that is to come were over and done, and I, too, had earned my rest."

He lifted his eyes as he thought it and met the eyes of Siggeir, blithe and smiling, and heard Siggeir say unto him:

"O best of the sons of Volsung, I am glad for thy sake and for the glory of us all that thou hast gained the sword. But even now thou art mightiest in the battle. What need hast thou of this new weapon? I pray thee, as a gift on this day that I have wed thy kin, give unto me this sword. At home I have a treasure house; in it there is mountain gold the weight of a war king's harness, there is silver in plenty, there is iron, and huge-wrought amber. All this shall be a gift for thee. But this sword that came to my wedding, methinks it meet that it lie on my knees in the council and uphold me in the fight."

But Sigmund laughed and answered and he spake a scornful word: "And if I take twice that treasure, will it buy me Odin's sword and the gift that the Gods have given? Will it buy me again the right to stand between the world's two mightiest kings with a longed-for thing in my hand, that none of their might could gain them? When men come buying thine iron and amber, dost thou sell thine honor too? Do they wrap it in cloth of the linden, or carry it away like ore from the earth? And shall you think my honor a matter of lesser worth? The sword came to thy wedding, Goth King, but to thy hand it never came, and for that dost thine envy make thee deal me this word of shame."

Black then was the heart of Siggeir and his face grew pale, then red, but he hid his hatred with a smile and spake unto Sigmund:

"Nay, I crave pardon, Signy's kinsman. I hold thine honor as mine own, and thee and thine I love as mine own. My heart's desire hath taught my tongue ill words and hasty. Take ye this as a sign of my good will and love: I bid thee now, King Volsung, to come to the home of the Goth Kings; thee, and thy brave sons, and thy dukes and earls of battle, as our most honored guests. Abide thou there the winter over so that the dark and dreary days will be bright with thy presence and that Signy, in the new land, may have about her the faces of those she loves."

Then speedily answered Volsung: "No king of earth might scorn such noble bidding, Siggeir, and I will surely come. But let two months pass over, for here in our fields and woodlands is much that needs be done and as a people's king I must see to the doing of it. But you and your host abide with us and of all my goods be free. Then shall we two together make our way over the sea and together come to the Goth King's abundant home."

The smooth-speeched Siggeir answered him, saying: "I thank thee well for thy most kingly bidding; yet do not take it amiss if I wend my way in the morning. We Goth folk know indeed that the sea is not a friend to be trusted, but rather a foe full deadly. I bear a woman with me, Signy, the Fairer than Fair, and I would reach the shores of my land before the storms of winter ravish the seas. So I go to put my house in order and there shall await the honor of thy visit."

So it was arranged that on the morning Siggeir and Signy should set sail, though Volsung entreated again that the Goths remain with him. The feast grew gay again, and all made merry, knowing that their hours were short and before them lay a hard journey. But Sigmund, amid his singing and laughter, had foreboding in his heart. And Signy, as she sat beside King Siggeir, divined something of the deeds that were to come. For the wisest of women was she and many a thing she knew; she knew her way in the depths of the forest and on the wild uplands, and she had listened and heard the voices of the night till the will of the Gods was clear to her.

So the feast sped on and many a tale was told of bravery in battle and of valor on the sea: tales that even today some of us have heard so that we know a little of the glory of that time. Then the summer night, which in that far northern land does not grow dark, came on, and the high stars shone faintly in the pale light and sleep came to the world.

Now, while it was still night, before the morning sun had touched the hills, Signy came stealing barefoot to her father's bedside.

"Awake and hearken, my father. For though the wedding is over and I am the wife of the Goth King, yet the Volsungs are not gone. So I come as a dream of the night with a word that thou must remember in the day-tide and take heed of. Let Siggeir go with me and with thy gifts and gold in the morning, but do ye not leave this land, nor trust in his guileful heart, lest thee and all the Volsungs perish and the world be nothing worth."

And as Volsung heard the words of Signy, there came to him the knowledge that she spake the truth. He sat upright in his bed and kissed his daughter. But he spake:

"I have given my word. It is gone like the spring-tide ships. I must go, whether it be to death or to life. Yet my sons shall hear my command and they shall not go with me."

But Signy answered him, speaking swiftly: "Nay, take thy sons with thee. Gather a host together and a mighty company. And meet the guile and the death-snare with battle and with wrack."

But Volsung said: "Nay, my troth-word has been plighted and I shall not draw back. I shall go as a guest as my word was.

Of whom shall I be afraid? None need mourn the going of one whose days are almost sped."

Then Signy answered, weeping: "I shall see thee yet again, when on the Goth folks' strand thou dost battle, but in vain. Heavy are the fates of the Norns, but each man must his burden bear. And what am I that I should try to fashion the fate of the coming years?"

Weeping, Signy left him. For a little while Volsung pondered her words, then sleep overtook him again. When once more he wakened, his household was astir and his earls had gathered in the great hall to bid farewell to the Goths. Siggeir, arrayed in his kingly garments, stood in the center of the hall; beside him was Signy, with the earls of the Goths about her. So queenly she was, so calm, and so fair to look upon that King Volsung could not but wonder whether he had dreamed her visit of the night. Together they drank the farewell cup of wine; the horses were brought and forth rode the Goth folk and the sons and the earls of Volsung.

Signy rode proudly in their midst, nor once did she look back. Across the heaths they rode, down to the sea where the long-ships lay at rest. Then Signy kissed her brothers and all the Goth folk blessed her and gave their promise to shield her from harm. She turned to her father and with her arms about his neck, bade him farewell. Something, I think, she whispered to him then, but none heard what words she spake. Then Siggeir spake fair words and gave his blessing to the Volsung men, but his heart held them no kindness. The gangways were shipped, the last horn of farewell sounded as the wind filled the striped sails and the long-ship, carrying Signy, was borne out to sea. White and fair she stood among the glittering war shields, but her heart was closed on her grief, and not once did she look back to the land which little by little faded into the distance behind her.

How the Volsungs fare to the land of the
Goths, and of the fall of King Volsung

The days passed and King Volsung lived merrily and bravely among his folk. As the time grew near when he had promised to journey to the home of the Goth King, Volsung called his sons and his counselors about him and spake these words unto them:

"Remember ye the day of Signy's wedding and of my promise to visit the land of the Goths? That time is near. Nor will I hide from ye that Signy came unto me with a warning that Siggeir, her husband, was a base and guileful lord and that his words of friendship he spake only to draw us unto our doom. The Sword of Odin came not unto his hand and for that he bears us envy and bitterness. Now wise is my daughter Signy and her heart is brave, forsooth. Yet there are times when from longing and their own pain, the hearts of women wander, and this mayhap is such. So I shall not too much cherish her word of Siggeir, nor, since she has spoken always with wisdom, shall I forget her

[19]

words. My own heart could feel no love toward *Siggeir* for all his kingly bearing and gentle-spoken words. But shall a king hear murder when a king his blessing giveth? So mayhap he bids me to honor and mayhap he bids me to death. But I have given my word and the word of Volsung is beyond recall. I shall go to him in peace, whatever the fates may hold for me there. But ye, my sons, ye shall tarry here in this land and guard my realm right well, lest the name of the Volsungs perish and greatness die from the earth."

But with one voice they cried out that they one and all would go. If the Goth King bore them evil, then each would stand by the other till each by each should fall. So spake his sons and the trusted men of his council. Nor yet would they let it be otherwise, though Volsung pleaded that he go alone in some ships of the merchants. So great was his love for his kindred, and the people of his land.

At length Volsung said: "So be it. It is vain to war with fate. We shall go as friends together and be merry-hearted whatever doom may come. And my realm I shall leave in the care of the Gods, mine own forefathers."

So were all things made ready for the voyage and in the first days of autumn King Volsung and his sons and the men of his court wended their way to the shore where their ships lay at anchor. Gayly they went on board, a brave and merry company.

Their ships numbered only three, but even the men who rowed the oars were earls of the court, stalwart and tried in battle. They bent to their task. A swift breeze sprang up behind them and the ships sped out across the sea.

On a day toward nightfall they sighted the land of the Goths and, as they watched the shore grow plainer, they saw a skiff with a sail of grey put out to meet them. Thus came Signy, bringing to her father her last warning.

"O my father," she said, "it is strange, and sweet, to see again your face and the dress of Volsung men. Short is the time that is left me, though it be but for a word before the worst begin. Truly, my father, did I speak to you of the evil in Siggeir's heart. It hath flowered and bloomed, and the death-snare lies awaiting you. But ye have come before he looks for you. Blest be the wind that brought you oversoon and gave unto me this moment for warning. Turn back while ye may. Leave this murderous shore. And, O my father, take me hence with you!"

Volsung kissed his daughter gently. "Woe am I for thy sake," he said, "but I have vowed that ne'er would I turn back from the sword or the fire of evil. I have held that vow till today, and today shall I let it go? And look, my daughter, on these your brethren, how great and goodly they are. Wouldst thou make them a mock for the maidens, that when this evil hath passed away and they sit again at the feast, that it should be said of them that they feared the deadly stroke? Nay, not that. We shall do our day's work deftly. And if the Norns will have it that the Volsung men must die, yet the name of Courage dies not, and that name shall ever avail."

Signy wept as one sick-hearted. "Woe is me, for hope is gone. But send me not back unto Siggeir, to the evil and the scorn. Let me face the fate of battle. Let a woman know death from a foeman's steel, for that is better than life."

"Nay, nay," Volsung answered her. "Thy fate too is held in this and thou must return to it. Thou art the wife of a king and much good mayst thou do. Farewell! The days will pass and we shall come to think on this only as a tale that is told, this day when our hearts were bitter. And thou shalt know the glory of the Volsung men and the love wherewith we loved thee."

Signy kissed them and departed. Through the dusk her grey-sailed skiff moved slowly toward the land. That evening she sat in the high-seat beside Siggeir, her lord. It may be that he had watched and that he knew the thing she had done, for he was full of guile, and grim, as he thought on the trap he had laid for the Volsungs.

When the sun rose on the morrow the Volsungs went ashore, a brave and stalwart company. Across the heath they went and over the wooded hills toward the dwelling of King Siggeir. But as they reached the top of a hill, lo, there they saw the valley before them thick with Siggeir's men. As the wealthiest acre of

The Volsungs saw the valley thick with the spears
of the Goths.

the rich man is filled with waving wheat, so was this valley filled with the spears of the Goths. So King Volsung bade his men tarry and arrayed them in the battle wedge.

"For duly," he said, "hath Siggeir come to meet his guests by the way."

So the Volsungs formed themselves shield against shield. In the very front of them stood their great king and lovelier was his face than ever men had seen it before. He rent the peace-strings from his sword, the blade flashed on high and gleamed in the sunlight, and he cast the sheath to the ground. Then up the steep came the Goth folk like a moving forest of spears and the earth shook beneath them, though they uttered never a cry. And the Volsungs stood all silent; the only sound was the clank of swords and of shield touching against shield. But they had not long to bide, for soon the Goths were about them and the front lines of the battle met. Yet they raised no cry, but the hills and sky rang out with the noise and din of war.

But how can one tell of King Volsung and the valor of his folk! Three times the spears of the Goths broke against their wall of shields; even a fourth time, though many were slain and shields were battered and broken, their wedge of battle held. But now the shields of those in the first lines were grown heavy with the weight of spears that had pierced and stayed fast in them, and as the Goth folk came on yet a fifth time many a warrior cast to earth his shield and gripped his sword two-handed.

Bravely they fought, but in sheaves the spears came on, and at last the host of the Goth folk won through the wall of shields. Wild grew the battle then, and oft and again forth broke the sons of Volsung hurling back the foe. But all their might was in vain, for the Goths still swept upon them.

In the midst of the battle, in that place which had once been the forefront, King Volsung stood. For to himself he said:

"My feet are old, and if I wend on further there is nought more than this that I see about me."

And his foes drew away from him and stared across the corpses that lay before his sword edge. But he did not follow after. Then must they in front, pushed on by the thickening spears behind them, come up to bear the brunt of his sword. And so he battled, until all his limbs were weary and his body rent and torn. And he cried:

"Lo now, Allfather, is not the swathe well shorn? Wouldst have me toil for ever, nor win the wages due?"

And mid the oncoming foemen he threw his blunted sword, and their spears, leveled like the oars of a long-ship, bore him to the ground. And he fell dead, on the dead about him. Yet for a space none dared draw near. For it was as a great God's slaying, and they feared the wrath of the Gods, and their hearts trembled.

And now, though the plotting was long, the tale of evil is short to tell. For when King Volsung met his death the battle burned but feebly and all who yet were living were borne down before the spears. And so the din and the tumult died away and the earls of the Goths came close to where on the ground lay a mighty people's king, in that place where first he made his stand. Quiet he lay, but the birds sang still above him and they told how his death was as good as the best of the days of his life-tide. And greatly as his people had loved King Volsung, so now his foes were moved to awe and love and they knew that the warders awaited him by Odin's open door.

But the sons of Volsung, those giants of the battle, yet lived though worn with many a wound. Borne to the earth amid the oncoming rush of spears they lay bound among the dead. And mayhap for them was even a wearier journey ere they should reach the Hall of Odin and sit by their father's side.

And great was the sorrow of the Volsungs:

"Woe's me for the boughs of the Branstock and the hawks that cried
    on the fight!
Woe's me for the fireless hearthstones and the hangings of delight,
That the women dare not look on lest they see them sweat with blood!
Woe's me for the carven pillars where the spears of the Volsungs stood!
And who next shall shake the locks, or the silver door-rings meet?
Who shall pace the floor beloved, worn down by the Volsung feet?
Who shall fill the gold with the wine, or cry for the triumphing?
Shall it be kindred or foes, or thief, or thrall, or king?"

Of the fate that befalls the sons of Volsung

And so came the doom of Volsung, and the earls of the Goths laid him to rest beneath the grass. But his sons, bound, were brought to the high-built dwelling of Siggeir. Needless it is to say that Siggeir came not unto the battle, nor faced the Volsung sword.

So now as Siggeir sat in his high-seat there came unto him his chiefest lord, and he said unto Siggeir: "I bear thee tidings of the death of the best of the brave. For thy foes are slain or bondsmen. And here is Sigmund's sword if a token thou desirest, and that surely shall be proof enough. But think not that the way was easy. Many an earl hath stumbled who shall never rise again. And I deem, after this day's battle, that King Volsung was the greatest of all earthly kings."

Siggeir spake not a word save: "Where be Volsung's sons?"

And the lord replied: "They are without, and fettered, those brave and glorious ones. And methinks it were a deed for a king and a noble deed for thee, to break their bonds and heal them. Then send them back to their land and abide their wrath and the blood feud for this matter of Volsung's slaying."

"Thou hast lost thy wits," said Siggeir, "nor dost thou heed the wise man's saying: 'Slay thou the wolf by the house door, lest he slay thee in the wood.' Yet since I am the victor and my days henceforth shall be good, I shall deal with them mercifully. Let the young men smite them down, but let me not behold them lest my heart should angrier grow."

E'en as he spake these words came Signy in at the door, and with hurrying feet she came toward the place of Siggeir, her lord. She was wan as the sky before dawning, but she shed no tear. And she cried:

"I pray thee, Siggeir, now that thine heart is merry and glad with the death and bonds of my kinsmen, grant me this one prayer, this and no other. Let them breathe for a day or twain longer, ere they wend the way of death. For 'sweet to the eye while seen,' as the rede of the elders saith."

"Thou art mad with sorrow," answered Siggeir. "Wilt thou work thy brothers this woe when even I am willing that they should die swiftly and untormented? Yet, if thou will it, thou shalt have thy asking. Nor do I begrudge them a longer tide of woe."

Signy said: "I will it; O, I will it—'sweet to the eye while seen.'"

Then to his earl spake Siggeir: "In the first mile of the forest there lies a wood-lawn green. There fetter these Volsung men to the mightiest beam of the wildwood, till Queen Signy shall come again and beg another boon for her brethren—the speedy end of their days."

And so the Goth folk led the sons of Volsung to the woodland. There they smote down a great-boled oak tree, the mightiest they could find. They bound the Volsungs to it with bonds of iron and left them there on the wood-lawn. And by the light of the moon they wended their way back to the dwelling of Siggeir, the King.

But on the morrow King Siggeir sent his men to see how the Volsungs fared. "It would have been wiser and safer," thought he, "to have seen the last of the Volsungs laid dead before my feet."

But his men were back ere the noontide and their tidings were sweet to his ear. For they said:

"We tell thee, King Siggeir, that Geirmund and Gylfi are gone. And we deem that some beast of the wildwood hath devoured them, for their bones still lie in the fetters. And those eight who still remain are sore diminished of their strength."

And so passed the morn and the noontide, and the evening began to fall, but Signy could not escape the watchful eyes that held her to her house.

And the men came again in the morning, and spake: "Again

hath the beast been there. The bonds hold the bare white bones
of Helgi and the bones of Solar the bold. And the six that abide
grow feebler.''

Still all the day and the night must Signy nurse her grief at
home, nor was there anyone whom she might send with a message to her brothers. And again came the tale on the morrow:

''Now are two more come to an end. The bones of Hunthiof
and of Gunthiof lie side by side. And the four that are left have
but a little while to live.''

O woe it is for Signy! How often through those hours did she
turn her helpless eyes to the woodland and the place where her
brothers lay. Yet she made no plea though her heart burned
within her.

And again on the morrow the tale was still the same: ''We tell
thee now, King Siggeir, that all will soon be done. For the two
last men of the Volsungs sit there side by side and Sigi's head
is drooping, though somewhat Sigmund sings. For the man was
a mighty warrior. But the bones of Rerir and Agnar lie white
in the bonds, and their souls are sped.''

That day Signy strove not at all to depart from the eyes of
the watchers. All day she sat in the high-seat with face unmoved
and pale. She spoke not to any man, nor looked at any man. The
night came over and it grew dark, yet she stirred not. Nor did
she give any heed to the word which Siggeir sent for her. And
in the morning he must needs take his place on the high-seat

beside her to preside over the council of elders to which the folk
were gathering from far and near.

And again came Siggeir's woodmen, and their voice arose in
the hall: "There is no man left on the tree-beam. Only the bones
lie white on the sward in the bonds that bound them. The Volsungs are no more."

No word spake the earls of the Goth folk, but the hall rang
out with a cry—the cry of Signy. She stood upright before the
high-seat and thrust all men from her, then turned and fled to
her bower, swift as the red deer pursued by hunters. Even her
maidens feared to look upon her face. Yet at the death of day
she rose amid the silence and went her way alone. No man
watched her or hindered her, for they deemed that the tale was
done. And so she walked between the yellow fields and the green
meadows of the sheep. Long before she reached the wildwood
the night had grown dark. She had no man to guide her but she
needed none, for the path had been trodden well by the mes-
sengers of Siggeir who had come each day with their tale of
death.

At length she came to that lawn in the woods that lay white
and glimmering beneath the high moon. And she looked, and
lo, there stood a mighty man and he labored at the earth with
a truncheon he had torn from the wood. And the man was
Sigmund the Volsung!

But Signy had no fear and cried unto him: "If thou art living,

Sigmund, what day's work dost thou here, in the midnight and the forest? And if thou art but a ghost tell me then where are the Volsung brethren, those great ones of whom thou wert greatest?"

Then he turned toward her and she saw that his raiment was fouled and torn, his eyes hollow and weary, and his face gaunt. But he cried:

"Hail, Sister Signy! I looked for thee before. Though what should a woman accomplish, one woman and alone, when all we mighty Volsungs could do nought in Siggeir's land? Yea, I am living, and this day's work that I do is to bury the bones of the Volsungs; and lo, it is well-nigh done. So draw near, Volsung's daughter, and together shall we pile many a stone above the bones of our brethren whom the grey wolves have devoured."

So she set her hand to the labor, and they toiled, they twain in the wood. And when the work was over the first pale light of day was beginning to show in the sky. Then spake the white-handed Signy:

"Now shalt thou tell me the tale of the death of the Volsung brethren. Tell me the tale ere thou must hide thyself and thy wrath in the wood, and I must wend me back, sick-hearted, to abide in the dwelling of kings."

He said: "We sat on the tree; and well may ye know that we had some hope of aid from thy good will in our most bitter need. None had escaped utterly the sword edge in the battle, and so hurt were Agnar and Helgi that, unhelped, they were like to die. Though for that we deemed them happier. Then, when the moon shone bright, and when by the best that we could reckon, it was the middle of the night, lo, forth from yonder thicket came two mighty wood-wolves. Far huger they were to my deeming than the wolves I knew at home. Forthright on Gylfi and Geirmund fell these dogs of the forest, and what could men bound avail? Then and there the wolves slew them and long we heard them snarling.

"And what other tale can one tell of men so bound and helpless? Night after night, O my sister, the story was the same. From the dark and the thicket came the two mighty wolves and slew two men of the Volsungs whom the sword edge could not kill. And every day in the dawning came King Siggeir's woodmen to behold what the night had done and to take unto him the word he rejoiced to hear. And so came last night, when it should be my turn. Forsooth, when the first were murdered it seemed that my bonds must burst with the rage in my heart and the fierceness of my desire to free my naked hands, that vengeance might be wrought. Then from the thicket came the grey wolves, and the he-wolf fell on Sigi, and he gave forth never a cry. Then the she-wolf's muzzle was thrust into my very face. The Gods helped not; but I helped. I, too, grew wolfish then. Yea, I, who have borne the sword hilt high mid the kings of men, I must snarl to the she-wolf's snarling, and snap with greedy teeth. My hands with the bonds were struggling, and my teeth took hold of her, and amid her mighty writhings the bonds that bound me burst. Then I smote the beast with the irons. When I had slain her I turned and there lay Sigi dead, and the other wolf had fled to the dark night of the forest.

"I hid in the thicket until dawning and from thence I saw Siggeir's woodmen come again to gather the well-loved tidings. And as I looked, I knew how hate has grown in my heart and the days of my mercy are over. But I let them depart unslain, lest Siggeir should come to doubt that all the Volsungs had perished. But hereafter, yea, hereafter, I shall not turn back my hand nor falter while any of these who have turned the world about and who have raised Hell's abode over the God-home, shall yet remain on earth. But methinks it will be long that Siggeir shall sit at his ease in his high-built house of the Goths, with his shielded earls around, while I am a swordless outcast, a hunted beast of the wood. And didst thou think, my sister, when we were happy together beneath the boughs of the Bran-stock, that the world was like to this?"

The dawn grew lighter and Signy stood, with kindling eyes, and answered him and said:

"My brother, thou art strong, and thou shalt be wise. I am nothing so wroth with the ways of life and death as thou art, for I had a deeming of it when all things were seeming well. In sooth our woe may linger overlong, and the children of murder may thrive while thy work is weary and a weight for thy heart to bear. But I wot that the King of the Goth folk shall surely pay for his deed and that I shall live to see the day. But thy wrath shall pass away and thou shalt live long on the earth an exceeding glorious king, and thy words shall be told in the market and all men shall praise thy deeds. So harden thy heart, O brother, and set thy brow as the brass. Thou shalt do, and thy deeds shall be goodly, and the day's work shall be done though nought but the wild deer see it. And mayhap thou shalt not be forever alone in thy waiting, for the long days may fashion for thee a friend, to help thee in thy task. But now must thou bide in the wildwood and make thyself a lair. Thou art here in the midst of thy foemen and thou mayst gain from them what thou hast need of. Yet be not too bold, lest they carry too oft to the King the tale of the wood-abider. Ere many days have passed I shall see thee again that I may know full surely the place of thy hiding and send thee help and comfort. But, thereafter, it were best, O last of the Volsungs, that I see thee no more, if so it may be. But the Norns must fashion all."

Then she kissed him and departed. The day was near at hand and as she left the wood the first daylight touched the meadows faintly, and as she passed on between the yellow fields the sky grew blue above her, and at length the golden sunlight shone as she came unto the dwelling of King Siggeir. And so the morn and the noon and the even built up another day.

Of Sigmund's life in the wildwood, of the
gift that Signy sends him, and of the slaying of Siggeir, the Goth King

And thus the will of King Siggeir was done and he gained his great desire. The Sword of Odin was his; he wore it at his side and it lay across his knees in the council. He sent his earls across the sea to subdue the land of Volsung, and that folk who had lost their mighty leader and such numbers of their brave were now beneath his hand. And Signy, the Fairer than Fair, remained dutiful to him and in all things did the bidding of her lord. So therefore in his own heart Siggeir praised his wisdom and the cunning that had taught him to prevail over all men.

Now in a half-month's time Signy went again into the wildwood and, by her wisdom, found her way to the hiding place of Sigmund. It was as a house of the dwarfs, a deep and stony cave, in the very midmost thicket of the forest, and a swift river rushed and swirled over the rocks before it. Signy found her brother sitting beside the river watching its thunderous waters and her heart rejoiced to see once more so noble and so brave a man. He spoke few words to Signy and these were heavy with grief and sorrow, but ever his love went toward her, and men say that Signy wept that day as she left this last of her kindred. But none among the earls of Siggeir saw her tears, and her face was as fair to gaze upon as ever. Neither fear, nor longing, nor grief marred its loveliness. But no man could say for certain that she ever laughed from thence until the day of her death was come.

So the last of the sons of Volsung must dwell in a rough and narrow home. War gear and gold as much as he wanted he took from earls and the men of the merchants whose way lay through the woods. But he went not often from his thicket to fall upon them, lest too oft to the King should be carried the tale of the wood-abider. Alone in the woods he lived and he built himself a forge and was a master of the craft of smithying. Sometimes the boldest of the hunters who ventured deep in the woods would see the gleam of his forge fire, or the men who dared to fish the hidden streams would hear the ring of his hammer. And men began to forget the fate of the Volsungs, but among those who dwelt by the wood there grew up a tale that a king of the giants had awakened from the place where they slept in the heart of the mountains and had come down to dwell in a cave that once had belonged to the dwarfs. And the men who dwelt by the wood said:

"It is aught but well to come near his house door or to wander in that part of the forest, for he is a tyrannous lord and a lover of gold and goods."

So the years passed and Signy still sat beside the King of the Goth folk. And in her court were men and maids ready to do her bidding, because they worshiped her kindness and her loveliness and because they remembered the wrongs that she had suffered. Thus it came to pass that on a morning in spring, as Sigmund sat on the green before the ancient house of the dwarfkind and fashioned a golden sword, he saw across the river a damsel, and a man-child of ten summers was holding by her hand. And she cried to Sigmund:

"O Forest-dweller, do not harm me nor the child. For I bear a word from Signy. Thus she saith to thee, 'I send thee a man to foster. If his heart be true and brave in time of need, mayhap he can help thy work. But hearken to these, my words, and pay heed to them: if thou try him and deem that he can avail not, then thy work is too weary to burden thy heart with him; let him wend the ways of his fate.' "

Then no more words spake the maiden but turned and was gone, and there on the bank of the river the child stood alone. Sigmund rose to his feet and crossed the river. He knew that the child was Siggeir's and why it was that Signy sent him. So he lifted the lad to his shoulder and bade him hold his sword and plunged again into the waters. But the young one was not afraid and fell to talking as he sat high on Sigmund's shoulder above the swirling stream. And Sigmund deemed that the lad would be bold enough, and he taught him and fostered him in the rough and hard life of the woodland until a space of three months had passed. The boy grew skilled and strong.

One morning Sigmund said to the lad: "I must go and hunt the deer. Remain thou and bake our bread so that it shall be ready against my return."

So Sigmund went forth and returned again at noon, bringing with him the venison. "Is the morn's work done?" he asked.

The boy said nought, and he was white and quaking as he looked at Sigmund. And Sigmund questioned him: "Tell me, O Son of the Goth King, how hast thou fared? Is the baking of bread a thing to frighten thee?"

The lad answered: "I went to the meal sack but something stirred within it, and I feared that it might be a serpent like that I saw on the stone last even. So I durst not touch the thing."

Sigmund laughed aloud and answered: "I have heard that there was once the son of a king who would not be scared from his bread for all the worms in the land."

And Sigmund strode to the meal sack and thrust in his hand and drew forth a deadly ash-grey adder. Then he took it in his hand to the door of the cave and set it down in the grass. And the king's son quaked and quivered.

Then Sigmund drew forth his sword from its sheath and said

to the boy: "Now fearest thou this, that men call the serpent of death?"

The son of King Siggeir answered: "I am young as yet for war, but ere many months have passed I shall carry a blade like that."

Then Sigmund went forth and stood by himself and leaned on his sword and pondered many an hour on the words that Signy had spoken when she sent the lad to him. At last when the moon had arisen and the pale night of the north had begun, he sheathed his sword and cried:

"Come forth, King Siggeir's son. Thou must wend thy way from the wildwood, for I can foster thee no more."

The son of Siggeir came forth and he trembled when he beheld the face of Sigmund. But Sigmund noted it not and bade the lad come with him. So they went in the night through the dim paths of the forest and by the time they reached the edge of the woods where the meadows began, it was the first moment of the dawn. There Sigmund stopped and said:

"King Siggeir's son, await thou here until the birds are singing and the day is well begun. Then go to the house of the Goth King and find Signy the Queen. Tell no one else aught that has happened, but unto her thou mayst tell all that thou wilt, and say this word to her, 'Mother, I come from the wildwood, and he saith, whatever befall, alone will I abide there, nor have such fosterlings. For the sons of the Gods may help me, but never the sons of kings.' Go then, with this word, and if thou dare to betray me, long shalt thou repent it."

Then he turned his back on the boy and strode away to the woodland. But the lad scarce waited for the sunrise ere he took his way toward home. When he came to the house of the Goths, he sought Signy the Queen and unto her he spake, but unto no one else told he aught that had happened. For the boy, though he had not the courage that Sigmund had need of, had the true heart of a king's son.

But Signy pondered long on the word that the boy brought back. And she spake to herself:

"How shall the people of the earth fare if the kin of the Volsungs perish and Volsung lies unavenged in his mound by the sea? I have given the best and bravest that I had, as I would give my heart and my fame and my body, that the name of Volsung might live. Lo, the first gift has been cast back, and shall I find a second gift before it is too late? And will even that avail?"

So year after year went by, until ten years had passed. Then again there came to that river before Sigmund's dwelling a man-child of ten summers. And the boy looked and saw Sigmund working on a helmet of gold before the cave where the dwarfs had once lived. And he cried out:

"Thou art the forest-dweller of whom my mother told me. I will come to thy dwelling."

[46]

So he took the rough stream and the waters rose up to his chin, but he waded through them, strong and straight, and climbed up on the further shore. He came and gazed on Sigmund and he said:

"It is a wondrous thing. Here is the cave and the river and all tokens of that place of which Signy, my mother, spake. But she said that none might gaze on the face of him who dwelt there and not tremble. But I tremble not at thee. Surely I must journey further, lest her errand come to nought. Though I would that my foster father might have been a man like thee."

Sigmund answered the boy and said: "Thou shalt abide in my dwelling. And thou mayst know that thy mother's will is done, since thou canst look on Sigmund and smile fair in his face. Tell me thy name and thy years. And what words of Signy doth the son of the Goth King bear?"

"They call me Sinfiotli," spake the boy, "and I have seen ten summers. And the only word that I bear from Signy is this: that once more she sendeth a man to help the work of thy hands, and thou shalt know in thy need whether he be of kings or of the Gods."

So Sigmund took the young one and they dwelt together in the wild and the thicket. Sigmund laid many a weary task on the lad and shielded him from no danger, but the boy was in nowise lacking in courage and hardihood.

Now a summer and winter and spring had passed over the

land, and summer was come again, when Sigmund spake one day:

"I will go and hunt the deer. Remain thou and bake our bread so that it shall be ready against my return."

So Sigmund went forth to his hunting and brought the venison home. The boy, as was ever his wont, was glad of his return.

"Thou hast gotten us venison," he said, "and we shall not lack for bread."

"Yea," quoth Sigmund, "hast thou kneaded the meal that was in yonder sack?"

"Yea," answered the boy, "for there was no other. But therein forsooth was a wonder. When I would handle the meal sack something stirred within it, something alive, though it looked but an ashen stick. But the meal must into the oven, since we were lacking bread, and so it all is kneaded together and the wonder is baked and dead."

Then Sigmund laughed and answered: "Thou hast kneaded up therein the deadliest of all adders. So refrain from the bread tonight, lest harm should come to thee from it."

For here the tale tells of a thing to be marveled at, that Sigmund, alone of all earthly kings, had within him the power to handle adders and other deadly creatures without harm, and to drink unscathed of venom. And Sinfiotli was so wrought that no sting of a creeping thing could harm his body.

Now Sigmund rejoiced that the boy had borne himself so

bravely and his heart filled with tenderness toward him. And he taught him how to wield his sword and how to be skilled and strong in the feats of war, and the lad was always eager and fierce in combat. So the years passed as they shared the dangers of the deep forest and gathered from the men of the Goths and the merchants what gold and silver they had need of, and what other goods.

One day, when a space of three years or more had passed, Sinfiotli spake to Sigmund:

"Surely, when I left the dwelling of kings and came unto thy dwelling, I had a craft to learn and thou hadst a lesson to teach. Many things hast thou taught me. But how long must I tarry before I shall fashion something great? Come, Master, make me a master that I may do the deeds of a man."

Sigmund's face was dark as he answered and his eyes glowed fiercely. "This is the deed of thy mastery—we twain shall slay my foe. But how if that foe were thy father?"

And Sigmund told the tale of Siggeir's treachery and he said: "Now think upon it: will thy heart be strong enough to endure the curse that shall last as long as thou shalt live . . . that thou art the man who slew thy father and amended wrong with wrong. Yet, if the Gods have made thee a man unlike all men, for thou dost not start nor grow pale, can I forbear to use the thing they have fashioned? The name of the Volsungs must not perish nor the evil they have borne be unavenged."

[49]

Then Sinfiotli laughed aloud and said: "I know indeed that Signy is my mother and aught that she asked would I do. But is the fox of the king folk my father? He never gave me a blessing, but spake many a cursing. Have I, in truth, any father save thou who hast cherished my life? Lo, my hand is ready to strike what stroke thou wilt. I am the sword of the Gods and thine hand shall hold the hilt."

Fierce then glowed the eyes of King Sigmund, for he knew that the time was come when King Siggeir should be destroyed by the curse that he himself had fashioned. And of what should come after, be it evil days or happy, the Gods should decide.

So Sigmund and Sinfiotli waited in the wildwood until the time should best serve their plans. Then when the first of the winter was upon them and the nights grew long and dark, they went forth unto Siggeir's dwelling. They chose the hour of twilight when, as Sinfiotli remembered, the day watch had departed and the watch of the night was not yet set. They made their entrance by a passage that Sinfiotli knew and hid themselves in a chamber where the largest wine casks were kept. It was close by the feast hall; no man came thereto but now and again the wine lord to draw King Siggeir's wine. And he discovered them not. They could see the torches shine and hear the laughter of the people and the sound of music and of beakers touching one against the other. The face of Sigmund was calm and his eyes were clear and bright; but Sinfiotli was pale, and fierce was his eagerness to begin the fray.

Now it happened that two little children, the youngest born of Queen Signy, were playing about the hall with a golden toy. They trundled it here and there and came exceeding close to the lurking place of Sigmund and Sinfiotli. Suddenly, without warning, there fell a ring from the toy and rolled in among the wine casks and dropped at Sigmund's feet. The children, running after it, came face to face with the two hiding there and turned and fled before they could hold them. Then Sigmund and Sinfiotli leapt to their feet and drew their swords, for the children had cried their presence to the banquet hall, and they could hear the din and the tumult surging toward them.

Soon the battle swept about them and the naked blades leapt out, but Sigmund stood firm in the midst of the onslaught and stirred no more for the sword strokes than the oldest oak in the wood shakes when the herd boy whittles at it. His sword flashed, and oft through the tangle of blades before him men would behold the clear godlike gaze of his eyes and, amazed, would forget the battle till it swept them on again. Sigmund stood his place and moved neither backward nor forward. But fiercely Sinfiotli went wherever the spears were thickest and many there were who fell before his sword, till he slipped in the blood and fell. Then the tale was short enough. The earls encompassed Sigmund and bore him to the earth unwounded and cast bonds about him, and Sinfiotli too they bound. Then, when the hall was washed of blood, the Goth folk went to slumber. But a long while Siggeir lay awake and plotted. Nothing that the days of his kingship had given him, nothing that he had accomplished seemed aught, so long as he had failed to quench utterly the kin of the Volsungs. So long as Sigmund and Sinfiotli lived there was no peace for Siggeir.

So when the first grey dawn appeared Siggeir ordered his bondsmen to build an earthen mound, and this house of earth was divided into two chambers by a huge stone. And in this house of death, each in his separate chamber, Sigmund and Sinfiotli were placed—to live as long as they might. And when they brought them, Sinfiotli was dull and weary and looked at nought; but Sigmund came fresh and clear-eyed and even as he sat within the walls of earth a song was in his heart. And Siggeir dared not mock him, as he had a will to do, but turned and went his way when the bondsmen brought the turfs for the roof to close them in.

By then it was the close of day, and lo, now, Signy, pale but eager, came hurrying through the dusk to the place where the builders worked. With unwilling and lingering hands they had roofed over the grave of Sigmund, but above Sinfiotli they had not yet finished and a place still was open. And Signy gave gold to the bondsmen and promised them favor in the days to come if they would be forever silent of the thing she did. And they promised. Then Signy drew forth something hidden in wrappings of wheat straw and swiftly she cast it into Sinfiotli's place. Then she turned quickly and was lost in a moment in the deepening dusk. The bondsmen deemed that her gift was food. They put the last thatch on the roof; then they too departed to their slumber now that the dwelling of death was built.

Then when the bondsmen had departed and all was silent, Sigmund heard Sinfiotli call through the stone: "Signy hath sent me swine's flesh in wrappings of wheaten straw."

Then he fell silent and Sigmund heard him moving but no word came from him.

"What hath betided?" cried Sigmund. "Is an adder in the meat?"

His foster son laughed aloud: "Yea, a bitter adder. Here is the Sword of the Branstock! I have felt its hilt before and know these letters carved on its shining blade. O my mother, now shall we live! O mother, mother of kings! I love thee!"

Then Sigmund heard the sword point smite against the stone and slowly amid the darkness he heard it grinding through as Sinfiotli bore upon it.

At last he cried out: "It cometh, my son! It cleaves the stone!"

Then in the darkness of that grave mound Sigmund stood up and with his naked hand took hold of the point of the sword where it had pierced the stone. Then back and forth they drew the Sword of Odin. Desperately in the darkness Sigmund and Sinfiotli sawed, back and forth, pushing and pulling, until at length they cleft the stone.

Then they met and kissed together. Then again they heaved and hewed full hard till the rafters were burst open and once more they saw the stars. They leapt forth and neither had need to ask the other whither their way led.

They took the night watch sleeping, and slew them. And then they fell on the faggots piled high for the winter fires. They piled the oak trees that lay ready cut, and when the oak logs were gone, they dragged the ash and the rowan until they had built a mighty wall about the dwelling of Siggeir. Then they laid the torch to it, and drew their swords, and watched the flames mount to the rafters of the hall. Sigmund stood by the gable door and Sinfiotli took his place by the door that was used by the women. None could escape past their swords.

The crackling of the flames aroused King Siggeir and his folk and from the depth of the hall the King cried out:

"Who lit the fire I burn in, and what shall buy me peace? Will ye take my heaped-up treasure, or half my father's kingdom? O toilers at the oar, O wasters of the sea, take thou the gifts I offer and give us freedom."

But a great voice cried o'er the fire: "Nay, we are not such men. We are not toilers at the oar, nor wasters of the sea. We will have the gold and silver when we need such things. But now we think on our fathers and the avenging of our kin. Not all thy kingdom, King Siggeir, nor all thy treasure, can buy thee life and peace. For now is the hour come that springs from thy own murderous deeds. It is the death-doomed and buried who destroy thee—Sigmund the Volsung, and Sinfiotli, Signy's son."

Then indeed did fear fall on the earl folk and their hope was gone. Then again the great voice cried:

"Ye women of the Goth folk, come forth upon your ways. And thou, Signy my sister, come thou forth, that once more beneath the boughs of the Branstock we twain may dwell together."

The white-faced women came hurrying forth and passed by Sigmund and Sinfiotli unharmed. But the feet of Signy came not near the door. The flames crept forward and the pearls of the throne of Siggeir shrank in the fiery heat.

Then the men of war surged to the doors, but at one the sword of Sinfiotli flashed in the narrow lane and the other Sigmund guarded. And the earls shrank back.

Lo now to the women's doorway Signy came, clad in her queenly raiment. She paused before Sinfiotli and spake to him:

"O mightiest son, it is best now that we part in this day of doom. Long have I toiled and suffered that this day should come about. And the thought of this day and the thought of you have long been as one to me. And now I take leave of you both—and willingly I go to my rest. Nor do I deem the days of thy life will be long to weary thee. But let thy soul, I charge thee, prevail over all evil, that thou mayst leave behind a goodly tale and thy short day be glorious. Farewell, my son."

She kissed him and departed, and went unto Sigmund. The sky was beginning to grow light with the coming of morning and as Sigmund looked upon her face he deemed that it was as fair and lovely as ever. Yet her tears were falling as she spake to him:

"My youth was happy; but mayhap this is the best hour of my life, which so soon will reach its end. I come to greet you, Sigmund, and then I must wend my way again. For I choose to sleep by the side of my lord Siggeir, and not to leave him. Yet fear not that I shall forget thee. I shall see thee in my dreams once more a mighty king beneath the boughs of the Branstock, with thy earls and lords about thee. And there shall ye all re-member how I loved the Volsung name and labored long for its glory. And hear thou this, O Sigmund: Sinfiotli, who aided thee to thy revenge, Sinfiotli, who hath encompassed King Siggeir with this sea of deadly fire and who brake the grave asunder— Sinfiotli is not the son of Siggeir! Thine and mine he is—a gift that the Gods have given that the name of the Volsungs might not perish. Look, look! Could another helper have done this deed with thee?"

And even as she spake, the red flames mounted higher and

swept over the golden roofs of Siggeir. Signy turned to Sigmund: "Farewell, my brother. I go now to sleep beside my lord."

And soft and sweet she kissed him ere she turned to go. Not once did she turn back from the flame and ruin, and Sigmund's eyes followed her with love, as fair in the fashion of queens she passed on to the heart of the hall.

And then, after the passing of only a moment, King Siggeir's roof-tree shuddered and fell and the huge walls clashed together. Such was the end of King Siggeir who would rule men by treachery and force, and of Signy, the Fairer than Fair, who perished with him.

How Sigmund cometh to the land of the
Volsungs again, and of the death of Sinfiotli, his son.

And so Sigmund returned to the land of the Volsungs, taking Sinfiotli with him. Once more Sigmund dwelt beneath the boughs of the Branstock with his earls and his lords about him, and his days were full of joy. But often he thought of Signy and he often spake her name, remembering how she had given all that the Volsungs might not perish but endure for greater things.

And Sigmund took for his queen a daughter of the king folk, Borghild by name. She was fair and lovely to look upon.

Sinfiotli became a mighty warrior and all men marveled at his deeds. He went forth against the enemies of the Volsungs and always was he in the very forefront of the battle. Then returning from his conquests he waited the long winter through in the hall of Sigmund, but for only a little while did he enjoy the songs and laughter and the days of peace. Then would he remember the word of Signy, his mother, that his days should not be long, and he would grow restless to perform new deeds so that he might leave behind him a tale of bravery and glory.

So when the spring was come again Sinfiotli put his ships to sea. His fellow in this war was Gudrod, a brother of Queen Borghild. They had plighted their troth to fight together and to share evenly the spoils of conquest. A long way over the sea-flood they landed their ships and went ashore against a powerful folk king and overcame him, after a mighty battle. And on the next morning Gudrod said to Sinfiotli: "Let us divide the spoils here on the shore before we sail our ways."

Sinfiotli laughed, and answered: "Why should two kings spend their days bargaining like merchants? I will come again in the even and look on thy work and take the share thou hast given me."

Then he went his ways and returned again in the even. Gudrod had shared the spoil. His pile indeed was the smaller, but Sinfiotli looked thereon and saw that the brother of Borghild lost nothing thereby. His horses were clean-limbed and strong and his cattle fat and sleek. His war gear was fair and shining; the raiment and the household goods that he took to himself were new and of the finest quality. His thralls were young and stalwart. Sinfiotli then looked on that which Gudrod had put aside for him. There was much in quantity, but the horses were old and the cattle thin-ribbed. The war gear was spoilt and the raiment and household goods were much used and of little value. The thralls were the old and the weak and the witless.

When Sinfiotli's men beheld it, great was their wrath. But Sinfiotli laughed and said:

"It hath been a good day's work. Thou hast done well, Gudrod, to sift the chaff from the wheat. It is meet that warriors should not burden their ships with things of little worth."

Then he cried across the sea strand in a great voice: "Depart, ye thralls! Depart old, and young, and good, and evil, and take with ye the spoils of battle."

Then he turned to Gudrod: "But ye, ye greedy king! What now can ye give me, of spoil or treasure, to save thy life from my slaying? It is unmeet that kings should hear of a king who steals his gold, of a king who breaks his troth."

Then wroth grew King Gudrod and he cried: "Stand up, my men! Slay this wood-abider lest he slay us, his brethren."

But no sword leapt from its sheath and the men of Gudrod shrank back in fear. Then Sinfiotli's brow grew smoother and he said:

"Indeed thou art the brother of my father Sigmund's queen. Wilt thou then do this much for thy honor, this much for thy life? Meet me here on this shore in the morning with thy sword in thy hand, for I know thou art no coward."

King Gudrod answered nought. And so in the morning they met and clashed with sword and shield. The tale is short to tell, for on the third stroke King Gudrod fell stricken to death. They built a burial mound for him and within it Sinfiotli laid plenteous gold, for he said: "It was for this alone that Gudrod strove."

Then Sinfiotli and his fellows sailed over the sea and came again to the land of the Volsungs. But when they returned Borghild heard the tale of her brother's death and came into the great hall where Sigmund welcomed Sinfiotli and the kings were feasting together. She stood before King Sigmund, and her face was pale.

"I charge thee now, King Sigmund, as thou art Lord of the Volsungs, tell me of my brother, and why cometh he not from the sea?"

But Sinfiotli answered: "The tale hath come to thee and thou knowest full well. Our swords met in the island. And there thy brother abideth, for his hand was worser than mine."

Borghild heeded him never a whit, but cried on Sigmund and said: "I charge thee now, King Sigmund, as thou art Lord of the Volsungs, drive out this wolf of the king folk, ere he slay all thine house and kindred."

Then spake King Sigmund: "When thou hast heard the tale, thou shalt better understand. Thy brother kept not his oath to Sinfiotli, yet did Sinfiotli give him fair chance in equal combat. Nay, Sinfiotli need not atone for any slain in the sword field. Yet for the love I bear thee and because thou lovest me well, and because thy brother was mighty, I will lay down a death ransom for him, a great heap of the ruddy gold."

But Borghild answered no word and her heart within her was cold and grim. She left the feasting hall and lay for a space in her bower. She brooded there and spake with none. Then again on the morrow she came to Sigmund the King, and she said that her wrath had left her and that she was well content if the King would give a death ransom for her brother. Thereupon she kissed Sigmund softly, and kissed Sinfiotli, and sat herself down in the high-seat, seeming merry and blithe to all about her. Then she asked King Sigmund to hold a funeral feast for her brother slain on the island, and he gave his promise.

So on an evening in autumn did the earls and the lords gather together beneath the boughs of the Branstock and fill their beakers with wine. Borghild, clad in a golden gown, moved among the feasters. She smiled at Sinfiotli and poured the wine for him:

"Drink now of this cup from my hand, and let us bury the hate that is dead."

So he took the cup from her fingers, but he held it in his hand and drank not, but pondered long over all his days and the deeds that he had seen. He sat by the side of Sigmund, and Sigmund said unto him.

"O son, why dost thou sit silent amid the laughter of earls and lords?"

"I look in the cup," quoth Sinfiotli, "and I see hate therein."

"Thou hast looked well," said Sigmund. "Give thou the cup to me."

And he drained it dry to the bottom, for you will remember how it was said of Sigmund that he might drink of venom and take no hurt from it. And the singing rose in the hall and Sigmund's heart was merry and he put all care from him.

Then Borghild came the second time and stood before the twain. And she said:

"O valiant stepson, how oft must I say it, that my hate for thee hath perished and love hath taken its place? Wilt thou thrust my gift away and shame the hand of a queen?"

So he took the cup from her fingers, but he pondered long over it on the ways of life and the deeds of men, and drank not.

Then spake Sigmund the King: "O son, what aileth thine heart, when all the earls make merry, and care is put away?"

"I have looked in the cup," said Sinfiotli, "and I see a deadly snare."

"Well hast thou seen it," quoth Sigmund. "Give unto me thy burden."

He took the beaker and drained it. The singing rose about him, and King Sigmund was happy and thought that these days of his were indeed good.

But Borghild the Queen came again and stood with the cup in her hand, and she said to Sinfiotli: "They are idle liars, those singers who sing how thou fearest nothing, for thou losest thy valor and art fain to live forever."

Then she stretched forth her fingers white and he took the cup from her hand, but he drank not but pondered long on the toil and the wrong of the world.

Then quoth Sigmund to him: "What aileth thee, son? Shall we never be merry and at rest from our labors?"

But Sinfiotli said: "I have looked, and lo there is death in the cup."

The singing and the sound of harps mounted to the roof-tree and Sigmund was dreamy with wine and with the years that were upon him. The noise of the people sounded to him like the noises of the woods and the boughs of the Branstock were the wild trees waving about, and mayhap he thought himself again a dweller in the deep forest.

And he spake to Sinfiotli: "Well seen, my fosterling; let the lip then strain it out."

Then laughed Sinfiotli and answered: "I drink unto Odin then, and the Dwellers up in God-home, the lords of the lives of men."

He drank as he spake the word, and forthwith the venom ran straight to his heart. And without a word or a change of look Sinfiotli fell, and the floor of the hall of the Volsungs shook beneath his falling.

Then up rose Sigmund the King with a great and bitter cry.

He knelt by Sinfiotli and lifted his head in his arms and none dared come near the King in his sorrow. It seemed to Sigmund as though he dwelt once more in the forest, and he loved this man alone. He lifted the body of Sinfiotli from the floor where it had fallen and bore the son of Signy in his arms through the wide doorway out into the night. And those who saw Sinfiotli as Sigmund passed deemed that at last his heart had found its rest and that his eyes no more were dreadful.

Sigmund strode through the night, bearing the son he had cherished. The wind was great and wild and the moon rode high in the heavens, now shining clear and now hidden behind great banks of cloud. Sigmund went on until the dwellings of men folk were left a long way behind and he came to the feet of the hoary mountains and the valleys long and drear, where there were no houses and no shepherds watching their sheep. And lo, before him was a mighty river, a wide and rushing water, with no ferry to carry him across. So he went along its side, as a man that seeketh for something, but toward the sea it grew even wider.

And now the moon sank in the west and the night was turning toward day. When lo, in that first faint light Sigmund saw a glimmering on the river and a sound came over the waters and a white-sailed boat appeared. Its keel ran light on the strand. In it sat a mighty man, one-eyed and seeming ancient, and his garments were grey like the clouds that hover over the mountains.

He spake to Sigmund: "Now whither away, King Sigmund, for thou farest far tonight?"

And Sigmund answered him: "I would cross this water, for my life hath lost its light. Mayhap there be deeds for a king to be found on the further shore."

"My senders," quoth the shipman, "bade me waft a great king o'er. So set thy burden ashipboard, for the night's face looks toward day."

So Sigmund laid Sinfiotli in the ship, but when he fain would follow, lo, there was neither ship nor man, only himself standing with empty arms beside the rushing river. He stood for a long while, gazing, then turned and went his way. And ere the sun of the noontide shone across the meadows, Sigmund the King sat in his high-seat. And again, as the months passed, he ruled his people and did the deeds of a king.

Of the last battle of King Sigmund, and
of the death of him

And now King Sigmund dwelt alone in the land of the Volsungs, for Queen Borghild he had put away from him. And he
thought of his loneliness and of his years, and that there were
none to carry on the name and the deeds of the Volsungs after
he should be gone. Now there was a King of the Islands, whom
the tale calls Eylimi. He was a wise and valiant king, though his
kingdom was but small. He had one daughter, Hiordis by name,
whom all men praised for her wisdom and loveliness. King Sigmund too had heard fair words of her and deemed that in her
he might find one worthy to be a queen of the Volsungs. So he
sent an earl, bearing gifts and tokens, to the hall of King Eylimi
to ask for the hand of Hiordis.

King Eylimi hearkened to the message but he made no
answer, for that very day had another earl come to woo his
daughter in the name of the mighty King Lyngi. And Lyngi's

realm was close at hand, while Sigmund abode far over the sea. And Lyngi was a young man and eager, and grim and guileful.

At last King Eylimi said to Sigmund's earl: "Abide thou here and make merry with my men and on the morn shalt thou have thy answer."

Then he went to the bower of Queen Hiordis, where on silk she worked marvels with thread of silver and gold. He stood before her and spake:

"I have said that thine own word shall rule thy wedding. And now hath it come to pass that again two kings of the people have come to seek thy hand."

Hiordis rose to her feet. "And which be they?" she said.

The King answered her: "The first is Lyngi, a brave and strong man. And it will not go well for thy father, if he should be our foe. The next is Sigmund the Volsung, whose land lies far over the sea. Already thou knowest of him and the tales that are told of his might and his heart of a God. And though he groweth older now, men say that the name of the Volsungs shall yet be the greatest on earth."

And Hiordis said: " 'Tis true, my father, that strife may come of this, but my answer is soon spoken. Shall I, who am called the wise, choose other than the greatest of all kings? Shall I choose a lord who is merely young and fair? Nay, thou shalt tell King Sigmund that I deem it a noble honor to become his wife and to dwell in the house of his fathers."

Now the King's heart misgave him, but he must abide by the word of Hiordis. He sent great gifts to the earl of Lyngi and the message that Hiordis was pledged to another people's king. But to King Sigmund's earl he sent the joyful news that ere two months had passed Sigmund should come to fetch his bride away.

"And bid him," said King Eylimi, "to come with a mighty host, with sword and shield and war shaft, lest aught of ill betide."

And so the earl sailed across the seas and returned to the land of the Volsungs. And he gave the word to Sigmund. Then Sigmund made ready and with his earls rode down to the sea where the long-ships lay at anchor. They were a brave and goodly company and fair to look upon with their rich garments and their shining war gear. But Sigmund, remembering the deeds of his father, scorned to take with him all his people and all his hosts of war. Yet the long-ships numbered ten and those aboard were the bravest and most stalwart of his earls. So Sigmund went on shipboard. They hoisted the sails to the wind, and the beaks of the golden dragons left the Volsungs' land behind and brought them at length to the kingdom of Eylimi. Great was their welcome. And when Sigmund looked on Hiordis he deemed her both wise and fair. And Hiordis was exceeding glad when she saw this glorious king and her heart told her of times to come full of many a noble deed.

And so Sigmund was wedded at a great and goodly feast. And

the joy of Hiordis in her lord grew day by day. Her father, the King, praised Sigmund too, and his might and his majesty, and forgot his fears.

Yet all was not as peaceful as they deemed. Ye may know full well that King Lyngi the Mighty was wroth when the gifts came to him and the answer that Hiordis was pledged to another. And he cried that he should have both the gifts and the queen, and that none should say him nay. Sigmund and Hiordis had been wed a month or more and Volsung had bade his men make ready the ships to carry them across the sea, when lo, there came word of a mighty host that had come on land from their long-ships and were gathering on King Eylimi's shore.

The heart of the Island King was heavy at these tidings. But Sigmund said to him:

"Thou deemest that my coming hath brought thee evil, but put away such thoughts. I have lived long and I know that the lives of mighty kings are not cast away, nor drifted like down before the wind. And I know too that Hiordis would have given her pledge to none but me. Come, we shall go forth to the battle and that shall be our latest deed. And whether there be life or death, the Sword of Odin shall lie no more at rest."

Therewith Sigmund brake the peace-strings and drew forth the keen and fateful blade. So the kings with their earls and men rode down to the sea strand. Few were their numbers beside the mighty hosts of Lyngi.

SONS OF THE VOLSUNGS

When all had left the castle, Hiordis came forth with one of her maidens and they hid themselves in the high reedlike grass near the shore, where they could see the battle.

King Sigmund's garments shone like gold in the noonday sun as he stood in the very forefront of his men. He called on each earl by name to do well for the house of the Volsungs; then he lifted on high the Sword of the Branstock and blew on his battle horn. That same horn had his father carried, and in many a battle had the foes of the Volsungs trembled at its sound, and many a man met his doom. The very earth seemed moving as the hosts of Lyngi ran like wolves of prey on the Volsungs and King Eylimi's men. But the way was not easy for them. On went the Volsung banners and on went Sigmund before them, and his sword dealt death with every stroke. His shield was rent from his arm and his helmet was cut from his head, but the slain lay all about him. His hair blew white in the wind like a ragged drift of cloud; like the darkness of an angry storm were his blood-stained, dust-covered garments; his sword was as the lightning that strikes and is gone before the hand may be lifted against it, and his voice like the thunder that follows after.

Then the battle grew weak before him and men drew back in fear and wonder from the light of victory that gleamed in his eyes and the song of his fathers that came triumphant from his lips. And Sigmund was no more worn and weary; he no longer felt that his life was almost spent, but with the strength and hope of a youth he waged the battle. And he thought to him-self: "A little further, and this river of strife shall be passed and at last I shall sit at peace, the king of the world."

But lo, at that moment, through the war shields, before Sig-mund there strode a mighty man, one-eyed and seeming ancient. His visage shone like flame, his kirtle was gleaming grey, his hood was cloudy blue, and on his shoulder he bore a mighty bill. He came face to face with Sigmund and lifted the bill to strike. The battle cry of the Volsung rang out to the very heavens and Sigmund's sword was high above his head, but its swift stroke clashed with the shining bill of the one-eyed and seeming ancient man, and in shivering fragments the Sword of the Branstock, the gift of Odin, fell to earth. The eyes of Sigmund were changed and the war wrath left his face. But the grey-clad man was gone and in his place the spears of the foe drove against the Volsung's empty hands, and they smote down Sigmund.

It was an ill hour for Sigmund's fellows. They fell like the hay in the field before the sweep of the scythe, and King Eylimi was slain in that place where he had fought bravely through all the battle. Soon there were none but foemen who stood upon their feet, and King Lyngi called his men about him, and he said:

"Who now shall say nay to me when I am come to woo, I who have conquered and slain the Volsungs?"

So, with his host about him, he fared to the dwelling of the

Sigmund's sword was high above his head.

Isle King to find the wife he had come to win. It was night by now, and the moon rose. When the last had departed, and she deemed they would not come back, Hiordis came forth from her hiding place. Her heart was half-dead with sorrow as she searched the field of the slain for Sigmund her lord. She came soon upon him, lying beside the heap of slain his sword had conquered. His spirit was not yet gone, though his hurts were many and grievous, and he had but a space to live.

His eyes were glad when they saw her, and he spake: "Thou art sick with sorrow, and I would thou wert not so young. Yet thy days shall pass as mine have passed, and it shall seem to thee but a brief space, as it now seems to me but a short while since my hands first gripped the sword and I but dreamt of glory."

Hiordis spake: "Thou livest, thou livest! Yet shalt thou be healed!"

"Nay," said Sigmund, "for my heart hath hearkened to Odin's bidding and mine eyes today have beheld him. He spake no word, for I knew already his message and the thing he came to seek. And now I live but long enough to tell thee of the days that are to be and perchance to soothe a little thy sorrow, and then will I get me home to my kin that are gone before me.

"Lo, yonder where I stood lie the shards of my Sword of the Branstock. Gather them together and keep them surely. Great has been the tale of my life and I have won the people's praise. And the Sword of the Branstock has been my fellow in the deeds

I have done for the Gods, but Odin hath today taken the gift that once he gave. I have wrought for the Volsungs truly, and yet I have known full well that a better one than I am shall carry on the tale. And for him shall these shards be forged again. It is of thy son and my son that I speak, of him who is yet to be. And I need not ask of thee, the wisest of women, to cherish and to guard him.

"Now, wife, put by thy sorrow for the short day we have had, for in sooth I deem thou weepest. Sweet and good were the days, nor must we cry to the Fates for a little longer yet, and a little longer to live. Thou shalt cherish my son, and joy because of him hath pierced my heart to the root. Grieve not for me, for thou weepest that thou canst not see my face; for tears thou canst not see that no longer am I sad, and hope shines in my eyes. Indeed I am waxen weary, but who heedeth weariness who cometh nigh to his father's house, after a long day on the mountain in the winter's storm, and seeth the light and heareth men making the banquet and the bed wherein he shall lie?"

Then the voice of Sigmund failed, but so mighty a man was he that a long while yet he lingered, as the night grew toward day; and Hiordis sat and sorrowed o'er him. But he spake no more. Then a long way across the sea the first light of day began. And when the sun had risen a little, Sigmund turned his head until its low beams bathed his eyes. And thus he died. And the sun rose up on the earth, but the soul of Sigmund was fled.

How Queen Hiordis fares to the land of
King Elf, and how she abideth there

Now as Hiordis sat beside the body of Sigmund and mourned over him, her eyes strayed toward the sea. And there she saw a shielded war-ship and a company of men making ready to land. And Hiordis fled again to the thicket where her handmaid lay. She spake unto her:

"My lord is dead, and here are we twain alone, and earls from the sea are landing. Give me thy blue attire and take you my gold and purple and my crown. And when men ask of us our names be thou the wife of King Volsung and I will be the handmaid. I have ever loved thee and believed thee faithful and true, and now I bid thee to this task and pray thee not to fail me."

So they changed attire. But e'en as a handmaiden was Hiordis tall and fair and gracious in her speech.

Now the lord of these men who were landing was King Elf the son of the Helper. As he sailed home from distant wars his ships drew near to King Eylimi's realm. They came close to shore in search of a place to land for they had need of water. As King Elf stood at the tiller and looked forth over the land, lo, he beheld the wrack of a mighty battle and the slain lying beneath their shields. In the midst of them he saw a woman kneeling, a queen with a crown of gold. And the woman looked and saw the ships, and turned and fled to the thicket.

Then spake King Elf to his men: "Here we shall find little water, for the brooks shall run with blood. But let us go ashore to behold what deeds have happened here."

So they crossed the field of battle and came upon the body of Sigmund.

"Look ye long," said King Elf, "for here lieth a mighty lord. These he hath slain were brave indeed to dare his sword and the wrath of his eyes. Would that I were one of his kindred, for I deem that none like him are left on earth. Let us fare to the thicket, for there the woman fled, and belike she can tell us the story of this field of battle."

So they wended their way and found the women and spoke to them kindly. Then spake up she who had been the handmaiden and who now wore the crown:

"We were of the Isle King's household, and I am the queen called Hiordis, and the man that lies on the field was mine own lord, Sigmund the Volsung."

Then were they all amazed when they heard that word and

knew that he who lay slain was the mightiest of all lords of the earth. And the sea king spake again:

"And this blue-clad one, who is she—so pale, and tall as a goddess, and white and lovely-eyed?"

"This is my serving maid," answered the woman. "She hath wept long over the battle, and sore afraid she is."

The King looked hard upon her, but he spake no word. Then, with the women, they went down again to the battle plain. There they set their hands to raise a burial mound for Sigmund. And they built a mighty house indeed and set the folk king therein. His throne was covered with gold and scarlet, and the walls of the house were hung with the scarred shields of the foemen and with the banners carried in the battle. But none could find Sigmund's war helmet nor the splinters of his own shield, and though his right hand was clenched he held no sword within it. And this was because Hiordis spake to the men, saying: "Our lord and master bade that the shards of his sword should go with our lady the queen."

So there lay Sigmund the Volsung, and far away are the blossoming boughs of the Branstock and the house where he was born. And have the Gods fashioned a folk, so brave and mighty, that in the end all their great deeds should come to nought? Nay, for it is with Sigmund like the mighty oak of the forest. The tree stands with the winds of summer in its branches and flowers and grass at its foot, and the wood deer dwell beneath it and birds sing in its boughs. It is a fair and lovely thing. Then come men with their axes and the tree lies low on the ground. The birds return from the southland and the place of their nests is gone and the house of the deer is bare and shorn of its blossoms. But now the tree is a golden war-ship, hung with shields, and it bears the kings and the earl folk over the far seas. It playeth its part full well in many a battle and brings tidings to many a land. Men reverence it as they do a king, and speak of it proudly. And such is the fame of him who labored in good deeds all his life, who died at last in the battle, and who lies now in his burial mound on the shore of a stranger land where the foe hath conquered.

And now when Sigmund was laid to rest, King Elf asked of the two women where it was that they would go. And Hiordis spake for the twain:

"This is now but a land of our foes and our lady and queen beseecheth that unto thine house we may wend and there live in thy care."

Glad was the heart of the King at these words and he bade all go aboard at once. They hoisted the sails to the wind and sailed by day and night until they came to the land of King Elf. It was a goodly land where folk dwelt in abundant peace and the Queen and her maiden were made welcome. And so the days went by.

Now the mother of King Elf was a wise woman and one

morning she spake unto her son: "I have watched them heedfully, these women thou broughtest from the outlands. I would know why it is that the less fair of the two hath the richer garments."

He answered: "She hath called herself Hiordis, the wife of the mightiest king, e'en Sigmund the Volsung."

The old queen laughed and said: "My son, was it not so that the handmaid gave the counsel when aught was to be done?"

"Yea, she spake the most," he said, "and her words were exceeding wise. And I deem her lovelier by far than all other women."

Then his mother said to him: "Follow thou my counsel and thou shalt win a goodly queen. Speak to the twain when they are not on guard and thou shalt soon find the truth. And again they will change their raiment, or I am nought but a fool."

He said: "Thou sayst well, mother."

So he spake one day to the women and he said to her who was clad in gold: "How knowest thou in winter that the sun is about to rise when yet it is still dark?"

And she answered him: "In the days of my youth I dwelt in the house of my father and ever I woke at the dawning, for folks must bestir themselves to the meadows whether the morning be bright or darksome. And I drank of the whey tub there; and now, though my days be changed, I wake athirst in the dawning."

[87]

Then King Elf laughed and said: " 'Tis a strange fashion that the feet of a fair queen's daughter must go forth to follow the plow."

Then turning to the other, he spake: "But thou with the eyes of grey, what sign hast thou to tell thee that it is almost morn when the heavens are yet black as midnight?"

Said she: "Long ago my father gave me this gold ring that ye see on my finger and a marvel goeth with it. When the night is nearly spent the ring on my finger grows exceeding cold and by that I know that day comes through the darkness."

Then King Elf answered, laughing: "Thy father's house was fine, and 'twould seem there was gold enough. But come now, tell me, did I not hear a-wrong the speech thou spakest? And is it not thou who wert the wife of Sigmund the Volsung?"

She smiled not, but answered: "Indeed thou speakest truth. But I feared the kings of men."

He said: "Thou didst not need to fear me, for had I known I should have held thee as mine own sister. For thou wert dear to my eyes and my heart was heavy for thy woe. But now I shall deal with thee better than thou hast dealt with me. For I shall bid thee to be my wife, and the queen of our people."

Then Hiordis said: "When the son of King Sigmund is born and the world hath gained a man, then will I accept thy bidding. I thank thee for thy goodness, and I know the love of thine heart. I see thy goodly kingdom and the peace that encircles thy land, and I will abide with thee. 'Tis enough, since none can bring again the past.''

Then the heart of King Elf was glad and merry. And that night Hiordis sat beside him on the high-seat and wore her golden raiment and her crown. And midst the song and the joy she thought of the days that had been and the days that were yet to come.

Of the birth of Sigurd, the son of Sigmund

The months passed peacefully in the land of the Helper and in the house of Elf his son. It was a land where men lived and toiled happily. The lords had no great storehouses of wealth, but neither were there any who suffered want. A child might go unguarded the length and breadth of the land with a purse of gold at his girdle and rings of gold on his fingers, and no harm would come to him. It was a country of cunning craftsmen who wrought many a thing that the men of other lands desired, and their skill was widely known. But though it was a peaceful land it was well guarded by more than fighting men. It was a country hidden and not easy to find; and it lay, a fertile, many-peopled strip of land between high, dread mountains and a perilous sea.

There was a man, of the family of the kings, called Gripir, who lived in this land. His mother had been one of the giant kin—those folk who are seen no more, though whiles on the

[93]

lonely heaths you can hear their wailing and their voices lamenting the days when they ruled the earth. A long way off from the sea strand and close at the feet of the mountains stood the high-built hall of Gripir. Men feared his dwelling, but the eagles loved this craggy spot and the woodland deer fed there. Gripir was a man of few words but of deep wisdom; he knew all the deeds of the past and there were times when he saw and knew that which was yet to come. He had borne no sword since the day when his father had fallen in battle and he had avenged himself on the slayer. Yet there was no fear in his heart. He desired nought but to note the deeds that had been and to see what should befall.

In the house of the Helper and his son, King Elf, there dwelt another man named Regin. He was beardless and small in stature and his visage was pinched and pale. Regin was so exceeding old that no man could tell in what year he had come to that land. He had taught King Elf as a youth, and his father, and his father's father. Regin knew all things and he was skilled in every cunning save in wielding a sword. So sweet was his speech that men trusted every word; his hands drew songs from the harp strings and he was a teller of tales. He was a Master of Masters in the craft of smithying and he had strange power over the wind and the weather and the ways of the sea, nor was there more to know than he knew about the art of healing.

And in this land Hiordis dwelt, praised and loved by all

people, till the day came when the son of Sigmund was born. And in that day was there great rejoicing and men's hearts trembled with the knowledge of noble and marvelous things to come. It was said that the serving women when they handled the linen raiment and washed the new-born child, shrank back from the bright and piercing glance of his eyes. But when Hiordis looked on the young Volsung, her joy burned like a living fire and her heart was proud of this, her son. She held him in her arms and told him of Sigmund, his father, and of the great name of the Volsungs. She spake to the new-born child as to one who could understand, and she told him of the death of Sigmund and his last battle. Then she gave him to the serving women to carry forth.

King Elf sat with his father and his earls in the great hall and their hearts were glad and merry. As they told tales to one another of great deeds that had been done, they heard sweet voices and the sound of harps drawing near, and saw in the doorway the white raiment of the maidens. She who entered first bore in her arms a burden wrapped in cloth of gold.

"O daughters of earls," said the Helper, "what tidings do ye bear? Are they of grief, or joy, or wonder, or fear?"

" 'Tis grief for the foes of the Volsungs and the enemies of the Gods," quoth the first.

Said the next: " 'Tis a wonder of wonders, and this the world shall learn."

" 'Tis a fear of all fears," said the third, "for the sword is uplifted on men."

"A joy of all joys," said the fourth, "for once come, it comes not again."

"Thou speakest in riddles," said the ancient Helper. "Lo, son, dost thou not look for mighty tidings to follow such strange words?"

Spake King Elf: "Women, thy words are greater than thy message, or else great indeed hath our dwelling become."

Then said the women: "Great indeed it hath become, for we bring thee tidings of a king new-born in thy house. Though long were the days of Sigmund, and great are the deeds he hath done, lo, greater yet shall be the days of him who is his son."

Then she who bore the burden stepped to the King's high-seat, and away from the new-born babe she drew the golden cloths. And she cried:

"O King of the people, mayst thou live long and be happy, as today our hearts are happy. Queen Hiordis sends thee this, and she saith that the world shall call it by the name that thou shalt name. Now give I her gift to thee."

Then, even as a man astonished, King Elf took the Volsung in his arms, and the ancient timbers of the feast hall rang with the shout of the earl folk. King Elf looked at the child, and the eyes of the child gleamed on him till he could not but think of the Gods themselves. And through him there ran the thought of all that the years would bring and to his ears there came a murmur of far seas beneath the wind and the tramp of fierce-eyed warriors and the sound of the hosts of battle, and then the low talk of wise men gathered together. All this he saw in but a moment as he bent o'er the new-born Volsung. Then King Elf raised his head and looked forth o'er his people and spake:

"O Sigmund, King of Battle, O man of many years, whom I saw lying midst the shields of the fallen and the silent praise of the dead about thee. Lo, thy dark night hath perished and thy day hath dawned again. What then, O mighty Sigmund, what then shall we name thy son?"

Then up rose a man most ancient, and he cried:

"Hail, Dawn of the Day!
How many things shalt thou quicken, how many shalt thou slay!
How many things shalt thou waken, how many lull to sleep!
How many things shalt thou scatter, how many gather and keep!
O me, how thy love shall cherish, how thine hate shall wither and
    burn!
How the hope shall be sped from thy right hand, nor the fear to thy
    left return!
O thy deeds that men shall sing of! O thy deeds that the Gods shall
    see!
O SIGURD, Son of the Volsungs, O Victory yet to be!"

Men heard the name and knew in their hearts it was the true one and they shouted it in the air. It went through the windows and doors of the feast hall. Men cried it in street and market; it sped over acre and meadow, through the length and breadth of the land, and all men's hearts were stirred.

And the Queen in her golden chamber hearkened and knew the name. Then she heard the women returning and again in her arms she held him who had been named Sigurd. And it seemed to Hiordis as if once again Sigmund lived and all was well. Her soul was at peace and she smiled on the young Sigurd at her breast.

How Sigurd getteth the horse that is called
Greyfell

Now the son of Sigmund grew in strength and goodliness and all men praised his beauty as the days passed over. And in the midst of the summer season Hiordis, as was her promise, was wed to King Elf, and they were happy together. The land was peaceful and the crops in the fields were plentiful and mid this plenty and this peace the young Sigurd waxed fair and strong. As the years passed and the child grew, he was keen and eager of wit and full of understanding, and moreover he was happy and kind to all. Often he liked to sit and listen while the wise men of the court met and spake of weighty matters.

Now Regin, the wise craftsmaster, had heeded well the young one. And one day he went before the Kings and spake:

"I fostered thy youth, King Elf, and thine, O Helper of men, and ye wot that no king had a better master. Now would I foster Sigurd, for though he be none of thy blood, I deem that he shall do abundant good in the days that are to come."

Then spake the Helper: "Yea, take the lad, for thou art the Master of Masters, and I learned all my skill of thee. But think how bright is this young one and teach him no trickery, for I deem that for all thy wisdom thy heart is grim and cold. And I love this son of Sigmund."

Then Regin laughed and answered: "I taught thee cunning, but I shall teach him none. He shall be no cold-heart, nor grim, nor evil-natured; nor could I make him so, for the Norns have fashioned him otherwise. And now, despite my cunning, how deem ye I shall die?"

And they answered that so mighty and wise was Regin that he would live as long as he listed and at last should lie down in peace when he cared to live no longer.

"Nay," laughed Regin, "one day it shall come to pass that a beardless youth shall slay me. I know my doom, though I have not power to change it."

So did Sigurd go with Regin and many things he learned of him. Regin taught Sigurd all that men taught the sons of kings, all save the craft of battle. He taught him how to smithy the sword and the war coat, how to carve runes, and to speak the tongues of many countries, and how to deal with the strings of the harp and sing songs for the delight of men. So Sigurd waxed wise in heart and strong in body. He chased the deer of the forest and slew many a wood wolf and bull of the mountains. He knew the desert dales and the heaths that the wind sweeps over and alone he fared beyond the outer skerries to the open sea.

One day he sat with Regin at the smithy and Regin spake of deeds that were done in the past and of wise and mighty kings until the lad's eyes were bright with eagerness and his heart swelled within him. Then Regin looked upon him:

"One day thou shalt ride out through the world as did the Volsung Kings. For this land is nought; 'tis narrow, and these are kings of only a peasant folk. Their earls are acre-biders and their hearts are dull with peace."

But Sigurd knit his brows and answered: "Those are ill words you speak of them that have cherished my youth, and a land that is fair and good."

Then Regin laughed and answered: "Mayhap, but I see by thy mood that thou wilt ride wide in the world like thy kin of earlier days. And wilt thou be wroth with thy master that he wants thee to win fair praise? If thou sayest in truth that the king folk cherish thee well, then let them give thee a gift that all the world shall know. Hearken to my counsel, and crave a battle steed."

But the lad was wroth and answered: "I have many a horse, all that my heart desireth. What more couldst thou wish me?"

Then said Regin: "Thy kin of yore were the noblest of all men; whatever of good they had, they still would strive for the best. Now do my counsel and crave of thy foster fathers that they let thee choose of the horses of Gripir the one that thy heart holds most dear."

Then Regin smote the strings of his harp and drew forth sweet music and he sang of the host of the Valkyrs and how they ride to meet the battle and of the glory that awaits the heroes among men. The song made Sigurd forget his wrath and he left the smithy with the music still about him. And that eve Sigurd spake to the Kings and said:

"Will ye do this much for mine asking? Will ye give me the horse that I need, for belike the day may come when I shall do the deeds of a king?"

Then answered King Elf: "The stalls of the Kings are thine to choose from, nor do we begrudge thee the best."

But Sigurd answered: "True, thy horses are fit for kings. But I ask now for a gift such as all the world shall praise. Give me a token for Gripir and bid him let me choose from the noble beasts that run in his meadow. But if I have asked overmuch of thee, forget this prayer of mine and deem the word unspoken."

Then smiled King Elf: "I see that thou wilt ride a long way, my lad, yea, unto the death at the last; yet surely shalt thou win the praise of many a people. Have thy way. We can no more hold thee than we can keep the sun from mounting up the sky."

Then Sigurd gave them thanks. Through the night he lay dreaming of many a matter, but with the first of the dawn he was on his way to the hall of Gripir. It was far from other dwellings and builded on a crag reft from the mountains. The wide meads, where many a beast roamed, spread about it, vultures flew overhead, and few were the sons of men who dared to pass its threshold. So Sigurd came to this place and entered into the hall. And there was Gripir, seated in a chair carved from the sea beast's tooth, and his sweeping beard almost met the floor that was green as the ocean. His gown was of mountain gold and the kingly staff he held in his hand was knobbed with a great crystal.

He spake unto Sigurd: "Hail, King with the bright eyes. Thou needst not show thy token, for I know thee. And thou needst not tell thy message; it was wafted here on the wind that thou wouldst be coming today to find a horse in my meadows, and that he must be strong to bear thee in the deeds that thou wilt do. Go then and choose. And I bid thee come hither again when thou hast won the sword of worth and art girt and ready for the road that lies before thee. Mayhap my wisdom may help thee then."

Then Sigurd left the hall, and he ran down the steep toward the meadow, but lo, a grey-clad man, one-eyed and seeming ancient, met him there. And he spake:

"Thou hastest, Sigurd. Yet tarry till I say a word that shall well bestead thee, for I know these mountains well and the meadows of Gripir, and all his beasts."

"Shall I give thee gold for thy tidings?" asked Sigurd. "Art thou Gripir's horse herd? Nay, surely not, for thy face shines like the mighty men my master Regin tells of, and it were as though I had seen thee other times, in my dreams mayhap, thy face and thy cloud-grey gown."

"Whiles I have herded the horse kind," spake the elder, "and the sages have praised the beasts of my breeding. There is one of them in the meadow. Choose him. That is the counsel of an elder who hath brought strange things about, and who knew thy father aforetime and other kings of thy kin."

So Sigurd said: "I am ready. But how shall I know the horse?"

Spake the elder: "We shall drive the horses down to the river that cometh forth from the mountains, and see what shall betide."

So the twain sped on together and they drave the horses before them till they came to a rushing river. Sea gulls flew above it, but none could hear their cry for the roar of the waters. So they drave the whole herd into the river and the horses strove to cross the stream. Many a brave steed was there, but the flood o'ermastered them; some it swept downstream, some won their way back to the ground, and some, caught by the eddies, sank in the swirling waters. But of them all one swam over and they saw him toss his mane of grey and gallop the meadows on the far shore. Then he wheeled wide and took the stream again.

Then spake the elder: "Hearken now, Sigurd. Time was when I gave thy father a gift that thou shalt yet hold dear. And this horse is a gift of my giving. Heed not where thou mayst ride, but do the deeds that are befitting a Volsung and a King!"

[106]

Then forth he strode toward the mountains, though Sigurd was fain to ask him many a matter. But his shape grew dim like the figure of a man fading out in the evening dusk, though the sun shone high in the heavens and the day was exceeding bright. So Sigurd turned and stood by the edge of the river, and the grey horse swam to his feet and came ashore with ease. And the youth looked upon him and deemed none but him good. And indeed, as the story goes, the steed had in him the blood of Sleipnir, the tireless horse of Odin.

Sigurd named him Greyfell because his color was the grey of clouds. And as Sigurd mounted, it seemed that the horse knew the son of Sigmund, so gladly did he carry him. Then the youth rode back in the bright noontide through the blooming meadows of Gripir and as he rode he sang the song of Greyfell, the horse that Odin gave, who swam through the sweeping river and back through the toppling wave.

How Regin telleth Sigurd of his kindred,
and of the Gold that was accursed from
ancient days

So the days passed, and Sigurd waxed strong and lovely. Moreover, he was kind and all children loved him well. But oft Sigurd looked toward the mountains and was fain to know what lay beyond them and was filled with longing to go forth in the world. And he said to himself:

"I dwell in a land that is ruled by none of my blood. The sons of my mother and King Elf are growing into fair youths and they will become the kings of this land, and will rule justly and well. And I shall not betray them, nor yet will I be their servant. Yet must I wait a little, till Odin calls me and sends me deeds to do."

Now again it happened that on a day Sigurd sat in Regin's hall and hearkened to Regin's tales of great deeds and of kings who had gone over many a waste and wild to seek their kingdoms. At last the crafty master said:

"Thou art King Sigmund's child. Wilt thou wait till these kings of the carles shall die in this little land, and then wilt thou serve their sons? Or dost thou wait for that day that shall never come about, when their banners shall wave in the wind, and they shall go forth to the deeds of war?"

Then Sigurd answered and said: "Not such am I. But thou eggest me too much, thou who dost no deeds. These folk are good and trusty, and the land is fair, and it lieth in rest and peace at Odin's feet. Yet I know that the world is wide and filled with many a deed to be done, and for such work was I fashioned. And truly my heart is fain for the house of my fathers, and full oft I dream that I hear them talking of the day when I shall come, and the deeds of glory I shall bring them. So when the deed is ready, it shall not lack for a man. But the wary foot is the surest, and the hasty oft turns back."

Then answered Regin the guileful: "The deed is ready. Yet it is best that I hold my peace, for thou lovest this land well, and thou lovest thy life and the peace of these days of thy youth. And why should he who is well fed seek out the hard road and the crust? Yet they say that Sigmund was thy father, and his hope was all in thee. But fear not; he lieth quiet in his mound by the sea."

At these words the eyes of Sigurd flashed so that the shield on the wall cast back their light, and his voice rang to the roof-tree:

"Tell me, thou Master of Masters, what is the deed I shall do? And mock not the son of Sigmund, lest thou rue the day of his birth."

Then answered the cunning Master: "The deed is to right an evil that o'erlong hath endured in the world, and to win an untold treasure that shall make thee greater than kings. Thereof is the Helm of Aweing, and its fellow, the War Coat of Gold, the like of which there is not anywhere in the heavens or the earth."

And Sigurd the Volsung answered: "How long hast thou known of this? And what right hast thou to this treasure, that thou seemest to give as thine own?"

"Alas," quoth Regin, "it is mine, yet none of it mine, since my heart dares not and my hand is frail. It is long since I first came hither to seek a man for my need. For I deemed in my wisdom that here I should find one who would prevail o'er this, and o'er many an evil of the world. But the years went over, and men were born and died, and I was no nearer to the end I sought. Then I looked on thine eyes in the cradle. And now I deem through thee shall come the end of my woes, and my days of waiting."

Then a while Sigurd was silent; but at last he answered and said: "Thou shalt have thy will and the treasure, and if the gold be accursed, thou shalt take the curse on thine head. But this deed will I surely do; for today the dreams of my childhood have bloomed again in my heart, and I long to look on the world and the glory of the earth and deal in the dealings of men. But tell me, thou Master of Masters, where lieth this measureless wealth? Do the swords of the earl folk guard it, or is it kept by stealth and cunning? Does it lie beyond the mountain wall or across the sea, or is it nigh at hand in these peaceful acres?"

Then Regin answered him sweetly: "Hereof must I tell thee a tale. Bide sitting, thou son of Sigmund, there on the heap of unwrought gold, and hearken of wondrous matters and deeds that I beheld ere the first of the kings was made.

"But first ye shall know that I was never born of the race which the Gods have made to rule the earth. I came of the race of the dwarfs, now departed. Fair was the earth then ere these short-lived people of the Gods were come upon it. And were we less than the Gods, though mayhap we lived not so long? We knew neither good nor evil, nor love, nor shame, nor remembrance of things past, but we did and undid deeds at our pleasure. Yea, we were exceeding mighty—bear with me, my son—for at times I can scarcely believe that our days of strength are over. But trust not thy life in my hands in that day when I most seem like the dwarfs that are long departed and dream most of my kindred.

"As we dwelt thus the tidings came that the Gods were amongst us and that men had come to dwell on the earth. Then were the days changed and we knew hope and fear, and grief. We learned crafts, the working of metal, and the getting of ore from the earth. We fashioned spears and bows, and built ships and sailed the seas, and the earth began to be such as the Gods had desired it to be.

"My father was Reidmar the Ancient, and now he was waxen old, and a covetous king. He bade me build him a hall, and I did, and it was exceeding rich and glorious. And he called his sons there before him, and he bade them be evil and wise, so that they might work his will. Then he gave unto Fafnir, my brother, a soul that feared nought and a hand that could never fail, and a greedy heart that knew no pity.

"And next unto Otter, my brother, he gave the snare and the net and the longing to roam the wildwood and the highways, and to hunt all creatures that match their cunning with man.

"And to me, the least and the youngest, he gave skill in every craft but pleasure in none, and the restless heart that remembers the past and divines what is yet to come, and knows no peace.

"These gifts my father gave that none could take back. We were less than the Gods and but little stronger than men, but one of our ancient powers was left to us still. We could change our semblance and at will become like beast, or fowl, or fish. For in the days before the Gods we had no certain form but changed our semblance at our own desire.

"So we dwelt, my father and my brethren, and Fafnir went abroad on his evil ways and there was no wrong he did not dare. And for me, I toiled and toiled at my crafts, and my father's house grew wondrous fair, but the love of beauty was not in my heart and I had no joy in the work of my hands. And Otter, my brother, roamed the wild lands and most often he made use of that power whereof I told you, and would change his semblance with the wood beasts and all things of the land and sea. And his woodcraft grew great and he knew all the cunning and wisdom of the beasts.

"Now as the years won over, three of the Gods left the halls of Heaven one day and came to see how the earth fared. They were Odin, the Wise, the Father of the Slain; and Loki, the World's Begrudger, who hath brought much weariness to the earth; and Haenir, the Utter-Blameless, who wrought the heart and the hope of man and his inmost yearnings. Thus they wended their way about the world and they deemed it fair and good.

"One day they came to the side of a mighty stream. Now this was a stream that my brother Otter haunted many a day because the fish were in it in great numbers. On this day he lay on the bank and dreamt of the fish that swam in the waters, and of catching them. As he dreamt, his shape changed into that of an otter, for 'twas in that form he hunted the streams. Then Odin and Haenir passed by, but they gave him no thought. But Loki lingered a little and he saw through the shape of the otter and he knew who it was that lay there. Guile rose in his heart, and he saw a moment to revenge himself on a foe; and he tore a rock from the rock wall of the river and hurled it across the stream and smote my brother Otter so that his heart's life fled away. He lay there in the shape of a beast, stark dead on the sunny meadow. But the heart of the Evil God rejoiced.

"Then the three Gods waded the river and Odin was wroth with Loki that he had done this deed. But Loki took up his quarry and the three wended their way until they came to a grassy plain at the foot of great mountains. And lo, there was a noble house, marvelously built, with carved stonework and pillars of gold, so smooth that the stars were reflected in them. Loki bade them, since the day was at an end, to pause at this dwelling. So the Gods passed into the hall and they marveled greatly at it, for it was fair beyond words, with beautiful high windows and golden hangings and shining golden pillars. And midst all this splendor they beheld a king clad in a purple gown on a throne wrought of the tooth of the whale. A crown was on his head, but he held no sword in his hand. He spake kind-seeming words and bade them rest themselves.

"So there was music and song, and they ate and drank and were merry, and passed for men of the earth. Then suddenly, mid the rejoicing, they felt themselves tangled and caught; and they heard the laughter and the scorn of the hall-abider, and his face and mocking eyes drew nigh to them; and they had no power to escape from their manlike bodies, so strong was he that day.

"Then he spake to them: 'Where now is thy mirth, O Loki? Come, Haenir, fashion love and hope in my heart, as thou fashioned men, that I may know fear and grief, and be sorry. And thou, Allfather Odin, hast thou come on one who is thy equal? Ah, I know ye are called the Gods, and are mighty men at home, but now with a guilt on your heads ye have come to the King of the Dwarfs. Time was when we knew ye not, and the world was to our liking. What now if I destroy you, and let Time run backward, and the Heavens lack a king? But nay, there is that which I desire more than thy destruction. In your power, ye filled my heart with greed, and that shall save ye now. If ye fill up the gulf of my longing, you can wend your ways back to your kingship and the home of the Gods. But ye must do my bidding, for ye know that I am Reidmar, and that ye stand there guilty of the death of my son.'

"Then spake Odin, the Father of Men: 'We have indeed wronged thee, and if thou wouldst amend wrong with wrong, we must do thy will. I know thine heart's desire, and thou shalt have the gold. But greater evil will come of this and 'twere better if thou asked not for it.'

"But Reidmar burned in his wrath, and Fafnir and I joined our fury with his, and we cried with one voice:

" 'Hearken, Gods of the Goths, ye shall die and we shall be Gods and rule your beloved men folk with bitter heavy rods and make them beasts beneath us, save ye do our will.'

"Then Odin spake in answer, and his voice was awful and cold: 'Give righteous doom, O Reidmar! Say what ye will.'

"Then Reidmar laughed and cried: 'Now hearken the doom I speak. Ye stranger folk shall go your ways when ye give me the gathered gold of Andvari. And Loki shall fetch it; and his hand that bestows no gifts for once shall gather and give.'

"Then Odin answered: 'It is well; Loki, who did the deed, shall bring the gold and the curse it carries with it.'

"But Reidmar answered no word for already he was dreaming of the wealth that should be his. But I loosed Loki from the toils and he went his way abroad, and he knew from Odin where he should seek the gold.

"There lieth a dread desert place in the uttermost part of the world where a mighty water comes roaring down over a wall of mountains. None can find the source of this stream or where it reaches the sea, but here in the rocky mountain beneath the great arch of water dwells Andvari, an Elf of the Dark. Time was when he had wisdom and knew all that befell in the world e'er even the dwarfs were come, but he has forgotten all save the gathering of gold. And now he heedeth nought of the summer or winter, nor has he ever heard of the making of men folk or the coming of the Gods to the earth, nor does he stop to tell night from day as he toils to gather treasure and store it in his house of stone.

"To this place came Loki and he saw the great fall and the mist above it, and thither he turned his feet. Loki entered under the roof of water and the hush of the plain was in that vault, and 'twas but bleakly lit by the sun. Here he spread his toils, and the tangles of his net showed not at all on the watery floor. Then Andvari, returning with gold, felt himself tangled and caught. And in that moment his ancient wisdom returned to him, and he remembered all that he once knew and saw what doom was come upon him.

"But Loki took his man shape and cried aloud: 'What fish of the ends of the earth have I caught in the pouch of my net?'

"Then the elf lamented and cried: 'Thou knowest my name full well, Andvari, begotten of Oinn. And 'tis the worst of the Gods, the forger and father of lies, who hath taken me.'

"Loki laughed and said: 'And how of the elf kind—will they do aught to save their life, when their weal is departed and they lie caught in the net?'

"Andvari groaned and answered: 'I know what thou wouldst have; the wealth that I have toiled and gathered.'

" 'Come forth,' said Loki, 'and give it, and dwell in peace, or die in the toils if thou listest, if thy life be nothing worth.'

"Full sore the elf lamented, but he came forth and led the God into his rock house. The twain trod on fine gold and the walls shone bright, brighter than the sun of the upper air. Great indeed was that treasure: there was the Helm of Aweing, and its fellow, the War Coat of Gold; and the world had nought like these.

"Then Loki bade the Elf King bring all forth, and he made himself a God again that he might bear the treasure away. So there in the dim grey plain the weary elf must pile great heaps of his hidden treasure, and Loki looked on, laughing. But, when it all was done, and the elf was hurrying homeward, something gleamed on his finger and Loki cried:

" 'Thou art guileful; thou hast not learned the wisdom and the might of the Gods. Come hither to me! I know the power of that ring to make more gold! Give it to me, for it shall be Loki's portion!'

"Then the elf drew off the gold ring and stood with empty hand, and his anguish swelled within him, and he cried: 'Thou hast all, Loki! But the gold thou bearest shall be a curse to the greedy hearts of men.'

"But Loki laughed and answered nought, and swift as his godhead would carry him he returned to the golden hall of Reidmar. We gazed with wonder when that world of treasure was laid within our hall, for it was as though the sun had come down to dwell with us.

"Then Odin spake and said: 'O Kings, O folk of the dwarf kind, lo, there is the ransom duly paid!'

"So he spake; but for a space Reidmar answered not but followed with eager eyes a gleam of gold that flashed on the walls. And lo, the gleam came from the ring on Loki's finger. Then spake Reidmar, scowling:

" 'Ye wait for my yea-saying, ere your feet may go free on the earth and your fear of my toils be done. Then you will laugh

[121]

and say: Fools of the dwarf kind! They have gotten the gathered treasure and let their masters depart with the seed which grows more gold! Loki! Cast down Andvari's ring! Or the world shall yet turn backward and know the Gods no more.'

"Then Loki drew off the elf ring and cast it down on the heap, and he spake: 'I am glad that ye take it, and the curse of the Elf King with it!'

"Then Reidmar laughed and answered: 'I shall have it while I live, and that shall be long, meseemeth. For Fafnir, the wise in war, is my sword, and my shield is Regin the Smith. And who is there powerful enough to do battle with them?'

"Then I loosed the Gods from their shackles and they grew great on the floor and passed into the night; but Odin turned by the door and spake, and his voice was like the voice of the winter sea:

" 'O Kings, O folk of the dwarfs, ye will rue this gold that ye covet!' But we looked not, nor heeded, for there on the floor it lay and our hearts were caught in its gleams.

"And sore I loved that treasure. So I wrapped my heart in guile and smiled upon my father and spake sweetly to him. I bade him keep the greater part of the gold, yet to give Fafnir for his help a goodly share, and to give me but a little handful for my work at the smithy. Though I asked for little, it was not little I desired. But Reidmar heeded not whether I asked for much or little, nor answered me, but stared and stared on the heaped-up gold and gloated over his treasure. And Fafnir spake never a word, but his eyes waxed red and grim, as he looked upon our father.

"The night waned into morning; still Reidmar sat motionless on his throne and gazed upon his gold. But Fafnir took his sword and I took my smithying hammer and we went apart in the world. I returned at even, heavy and weary of heart, and I longed to look on the gold, but fear was upon me and I durst not. And methought as I lay on my bed, drowsy with slumber yet not asleep, that I heard sounds and saw lights in the hall. But I slept and dreamt, till I woke to a cry and the clashing of metal, and I leapt from my bed and ran forth.

"There in the hall by the heaped-up gold stood my brother Fafnir, and at his feet lay Reidmar and the treasure was red with his blood, and e'en as I looked death came over him and he breathed no more. When I looked on Fafnir I trembled, for he wore the Helm of Aweing and the War Coat of Gold glittered upon him, and his sword was bare in his hand; and the hand and the sword were red with the blood of our father Reidmar. And it seemed as I looked upon him that he grew before my eyes, and he cried out in a dreadful voice:

" 'I have slain my father Reidmar, that the gold shall be mine alone. I shall dwell alone henceforward; and the gold and its waxing curse, I shall brood on them both together. I am a king henceforward and long shall be my life, and the gold shall grow with my longing, for I shall hide it here and hoard the ring of Andvari. O thou, wilt thou tarry and tarry, till I cast thy blood on the pile? Lo, I am a king forever, and alone on the gold shall I dwell.'

"His visage grew more awful as he spake, and I durst no longer behold him, but turned and fled. I fled from the glorious house that mine own hands had made so fair; and I had nought in the world, neither raiment, nor gear, nor gold. I came unto this land, and that was long ago as men folk count the years; and the skill of my hands and my wisdom brought me fame. I taught folk to reap and sow; but that generation died and they said that Frey had taught them, and a God received the glory. Then I taught them the craft of metals, and the sailing of ships, and the taming of horses, and the plowing the field, and the building up of houses; and that race of men died, and 'twas said that Thor had taught them. Then I taught their maidens to hold the needle and how the weaving could be done; but when they were grown old and dim-eyed, 'twas said that Freyia had come among them and given them their skill. Then I taught them tales of old, and fair songs, and the music of the harp, and their speech grew soft and sweet; but the youth of the land said 'twas Bragi had taught their elders. But it mattered not who received the glory, my cunning flourished, and I grew to be the Master of Masters. . . . Think how strange that a sword in the hand of a youth shall one day end all this. . . .

SONS OF THE VOLSUNGS

"Yet oft mid all my wisdom I longed for my brother's part, and envied Fafnir his kingship. I thought of his measureless gold when the kings of the earth would pay me out of their scanty treasures. And once, didst thou number the years thou wouldst think it long ago, I wandered back to the country from whence I came. Methought the moors had grown wilder, and the meadows lay waste, and the house was in ruins and open to the sky. When I came to the doorway, all was silent; neither owls nor bats haunted it, nor did the wood wolves draw near. But I went to the pillared hall and lo, huge heaps of gold, and to and fro amidst them rolled a mighty serpent. Then my heart grew chill with terror and I remembered how our race oft changed its form, and I, who had lost that cunning, was now a man in a deadly place. A feeble man and swordless before the foe, I knew that the serpent was Fafnir, that wallower on the gold. So I gathered my strength and fled and hid myself again among men folk, and the more vain was my hope, the more I longed for the treasure. Long years, and long years after, men began to tell the tale of the house of gold on the Glittering Heath, and the serpent who was lord of that fearful place. I knew they spake of Fafnir, and that serpent was my brother. This was ages long ago and yet in that desert he dwells, and no man dares come nigh unto him for fear of death.

"Then came thy kin, O Sigurd, and I fell again to the dreaming of dreams. I beheld the glory of the race of the Volsungs and

I deemed that from them should come he who would bring my heart to its rest. Ah, I fell to dreaming dreams. And some day I shall have it, Fafnir's gold and his craft and his heart. And when my hand is upon it I shall thaw away the winter and the evil he has made, and the world shall be young again, and my deeds shall be remembered and the earth shall honor me. Yea, I shall be God of all that is, and the world forever shall be young beneath my hand."

Then Regin spake no more, and his eyelids fell, and he slumbered, worn with his tale and the remembrance of old griefs. But Sigurd, the youth, leapt to his feet and drew his sword, and the fire blazed high in the smithy. And he cried out:

"Awake, O Master, for the day goes by and thou sayest that men folk live but a little space. Awake! For the day grows late and the deeds will pass us by."

Regin groaned and awakened, and he was heavy-eyed and weary as a man bowed down by a burden. And he spake:

"Hast thou hearkened, Sigurd? Wilt thou help a man that is old to avenge him for his father? Wilt thou win the treasure and be more than the kings of earth? Wilt thou rid the earth of an evil that my heart hath endured o'erlong?"

Sigurd looked upon him and Regin drooped and trembled before his clear and steadfast eyes. But the youth spake as before, and answered Regin:

"Thou shalt have thy will, and the treasure, and take the curse on thine head."

Of the forging of the sword that is called
the Wrath of Sigurd

Now Sigurd came again to Regin one day and said unto him: "Thou hast set me a task whereof none knoweth the ending; so I ask a gift of thee."

And Regin answered him: "The world must be wide if my hand may not reach across it for aught thine heart may need."

"Yea, wide is the world," said Sigurd, "and thou makest thy answer quickly. But this gift thou shalt not gainsay me; for I bid thee forge me a sword."

Then spake the Master of Masters, and his voice was soft and sweet: "The moon has grown from a slim and lovely crescent till now it hangs in the sky round as a war shield of the Gods, since first I struck my anvil to forge thee a sword. Lo, here it is! I have wrought it with many a spell and charm and all the craft of the dwarf kind. Be glad of it; it shall endure for thee through many a storm of battle."

Then Sigurd looked on the sword, but spake not a word. The hilt was golden and set with gems, and the blade was blue and cold, and the sides of it were carved with runes. And Regin spake again, soft and sweet:

"How likest thou the sword?"

Then Sigurd laughed and answered: "Its work shall prove it. See now whether this be a traitor to fail me in my need."

Regin trembled and shrank before the bright gleam in Sigurd's eyes. Sigurd raised the sword high above his head and smote it down on the anvil. But the blade shivered into fragments and the pieces fell to earth. And Sigurd's heart grew wroth:

"Lo, there is the sword for my right hand. There is the golden glitter, and the word that thou didst speak."

And he turned his back on Regin and strode out of the smithy, and many a day of the springtide passed ere he returned again.

But at last he came and spake to Regin: "What hast thou done, O Master, in the forging of the sword?"

Then Regin answered him sweetly: "A hard taskmaster art thou. But, lo, here is a blade of battle that shall surely please thee! Two moons have clean departed since thou last wert here and I have labored night and day. Mine ancient cunning hath surely left mine hands if thou praise not this sword."

And indeed the hilt was glorious with many a costly stone and the sharp edge gleamed. But Sigurd's eyes gleamed brighter and Regin scarce dared to look upon the Volsung. And Sigurd cried out to him:

"Regin, thy kin of the olden days were an evil and treacherous folk, and they lied and murdered for gold. And now if thou wouldst betray me, beware of the ancient curse, and set thy face to bear it. For he who would win to the heavens, and be as the high Gods, must tremble at nought on the road, nor fear to kill them who would stay him."

And he raised the sword high above his head and its blade flashed in his hand, and he smote the anvil again and again. But the life of the sword was departed and its edge was dulled and broken. Sigurd said no word, but he cast the blade on the ashes and strode through the door of the smithy.

On the morrow Sigurd went to his mother and spake unto her: "The shards, the shards of the sword that thou gathered for my sake on that field where my father fell. Hast thou guarded them with care? Where hast thou laid them, my mother?"

Then she looked upon him: "Art thou wroth, O Sigurd my son, that such eyes shine in thy head? And wilt thou be wroth with thy mother?"

"Nay," said he, "I am not wrathful. But the days rise up like a wall betwixt my soul and the deeds that I would do. And why shouldst thou fear mine eyes? Thou hast fashioned them, and 'tis the light of battle that shines therein. Now give me the sword, my mother, the sword that Sigmund gave thee to keep."

She said: "I shall give it thee gladly, for I shall treasure thy praise when thou knowest how safe I have kept it."

She took his hand in her hand, and they went their way through the house of the kings till they came to the Queen's treasure chamber. They entered and she turned the key in a chest of gold and drew forth from where they lay wrapped in fine cloths, the shards of Sigmund's sword. No fleck of rust stained the edges, and the gems in the hilt flashed as brightly as when the sword first hung in the hall of the Volsungs.

Sigurd smiled upon it, and said: "O Mother of Kings, well hast thou guarded the war glaive; well hast thou given to me the message of my father and the promise of what is yet to be. But now the days of thy trust are over. These shards shall be knit together and they shall hear the winds of war. They shall shine in the battle, and shake the thrones of kings, and undo the treason of the world. Old are they in glory, but now shall they fashion a new tale."

Then she felt his hands about her as he took the fateful sword and kissed her soft and sweetly. But she spake not, and in silence watched him depart . . . he had grown so great and fair, and his face was glorious, and he was young as the Gods are young.

Sigurd went swiftly to Regin's house. The Master stood in the doorway. Behind him leapt the flame of the smithy, and he looked dark and little. And his speech no more was sweet. He gave no greeting till he took the shards of the sword from Sigurd. Then he spake:

"Will nothing serve thee save this fateful blade, that hath brought evil and destruction on the house of thy father's father?"

Then answered the bright-eyed Sigurd: "If thou wilt make me a sword, nought but these shards shall be in it. And if thou begrudgest and would give me a dull blade of battle, it is too late, for the word of the Norns has gone forth. It matters not how much thou repentest that thy kin must lie low, nor how much thou doubtest that the deed will bring thee power, thou shalt have the gold and the wisdom of Fafnir, and take its curse on thine head. Thy lips have spoken, and it lies no more with thee to do the deed or leave it. Thou hast shown me the world as it was aforetime, and I see now the world that shall be, and woe to the tangling thicket or the wall that hindereth me! Nor will I tarry, for what if the serpent should die ere the first of my strokes be stricken? Wilt thou knit these shards together? If not, and a smith's hands fail me, then I shall do it. The Norns have doomed thy brother, and I deem this sword shall be the slayer of the serpent."

The gloom of Regin waxed great, and he said: "Thou sayst truth, for none may turn backward, but must wend on to the fate the Gods have made. Yea, this sword shall slay the serpent, and do another deed, and many a one thereafter. But fair and great as thou now art, yet get thee from mine house, for might in me ariseth too, and the place is perilous with my craft and cunning. Thou art wroth, but thy wrath must slumber till fate shall call it forth. Depart, lest our end o'ertake us ere our work is done. Go now, but come again in the night-tide when the full moon shines on the first of the May."

For a space Sigurd waited. He feared not Regin, nor any craft of the dwarf kind, nor what fate might hold for him. But his anger with the Master faded, and he was weary with his hatred of evil things and with desire for a sword that should conquer. So he turned and went out in the April evening and made his way to the house of the kings.

Now when the moon was full and the month of May had begun, Sigurd returned again to Regin. The King of the Dwarf Kind stood by his smithy and the light of the fire showed him dim-eyed and weary. And he spake to Sigurd:

"Hail, Son of the Volsungs! I have toiled and thou hast desired, and lo, there is the fateful blade."

Then Sigurd saw it lying on the grey ashes, and the hilt was ruddy and shining, and the edges pale and fine, and a gleam like the flame of lightning ran down to the very point of it and burned through the runes that were scored on its sides. No sound did Sigurd utter as he stooped down for his sword, but his lips moved as though the words of his desire spake within him. The blade leapt white over his head, then blazed like fire as he played it hither and thither, till he brought it down on the anvil with a fierce and mighty stroke. Then Sigurd cried aloud in his glory and held out the sword full length, as one who would show it to the world—for the edges were dulled no whit, but the anvil was cleft in twain.

Then turned the Volsung to Regin: "Now shall I work thy will. My father hath made me mighty, but I shall give thee the gold and the craft thou desirest, ere I wend on my ways. For now thou hast failed me in nought, and the sword is a wondrous thing."

No word for a while spake Regin, and he looked down as a man that pondereth deeply. Then he spake, and his voice was no more weary:

"This Wrath of thine hath cleft what is hard and heavy. It shall shear the light and soft; come forth to the night and prove it."

So the twain went forth to the river, and the stream was swift and full, and the moon shone white upon it. Then Regin cast on the water a lock of fine-spun wool and held the sword in the water's edge. The wool spun round on the eddy, but when it met the blade's edge it was sheared in twain.

Then Regin spake: "It is good, this sword that I have wrought. And now thy work beginneth. Thy Wrath is alive and awake and the tale of thy deeds is begun."

Then the sword, which ever since has been called the Wrath of Sigurd, was laid in a golden sheath and the peace-strings were knit about it.

Of Sigurd's ride to the Glittering Heath,
and of the slaying of Fafnir the Serpent

On the morrow after Sigurd had received his Wrath, he mounted Greyfell and rode toward the dwelling of Gripir, for he remembered the word of Gripir that he should return thence when he had won his sword and was girt and ready for the road that lay before him. So with the Wrath girded to his side, he wended his way across the wild heaths to the foot of the mountains. His grey eyes were bright and happy and he sang a song, for Sigurd's heart rejoiced that he had won his sword and his horse, and now should do the deeds of a man, yea, even the deeds of a Volsung. And when Sigurd reached his dwelling, Gripir greeted him with great friendliness, and they had talk together. And Sigurd asked of him how his life should go, because Gripir in his exceeding wisdom knew what things were to come, and what was fated to men. Gripir told Sigurd what his life should be, and the fate thereof, even as it afterwards came to pass. And

[139]

Gripir gave Sigurd his blessing, and Sigurd departed and returned, as the sun set and the evening came on, to the dwelling of the kings.

On the day following, Sigurd the Volsung went forth again and by his side fared Regin, the Master of Masters. They left the dwelling of the kings and rode throughout the day, till in the evening they had left the plain behind and the hills were about them. They wended their way higher and higher, nor rested till it was midnight. When they awakened in the early dawning, far away they could see the land of the Helper, and the valleys and meadows, but before them rose the sheer wall of the mountains.

Then spake the Master of Masters: "We have come to the gate of the mountains. Behind thee there is youth and rest, and many a pleasure. And mayhap I could find rest and a peaceful end to my years. We have come to the gate of the mountains. Thinkest thou we should fare further?"

"Yea, and what else?" answered Sigurd. "Unless thy tale was but lies and mockeries."

"It was sooth, it was sooth," said Regin, "and more I might have told thee had I heart and space to remember."

But Regin hung his head as he spake these words, and there was fear in his face. Then he spake again:

"Thou art grown wise-hearted and thou knowest my thought. It were well if thine eyes were blinder, and we each were faring alone. But times I dream that thou hadst neither father nor mother; that I alone have wrought thee, a bright and glorious thing, to work my will. Then my hope riseth and I behold the day that is to come and the world moulded to my desires. But then I awake and remember that thou art the son of Sigmund and the Sword of the Branstock is in thy hand. Ah, if only the world might run backward to the days of the dwarfs!"

But Sigurd heeded not the words of Regin, nor answered him. He leapt aback of Greyfell, and the sun rose and the heavens glowed above him like the bowl of Baldur's cup. And the golden light streamed over him till he seemed himself the very heart of the sun. Then Sigurd cried to Greyfell and rode swift for the pass in the mountains, and Regin followed after.

Day-long they fared through the mountains, and the way was steep and treacherous. And when the moon rose up and the stars were shining, they slept on the ground. In the cold dawn they wakened, and Sigurd was fair and strong as he drew the girths of Greyfell's saddle. But Regin seemed old and like a ghost of that wan land, and his words were full of foreboding. But Sigurd was merry of heart and no fear of Regin's could turn him from the deed he had sworn to do. So for another day they rode and rode through the desolate mountains and slept again beneath the naked heavens. Again with the first light they arose, and on this morning Sigurd donned his war gear. And Regin asked of him:

[141]

"What is thine hope this morning, O Sigurd, that thou array-est thyself in war gear to ride this world forlorn?"

"Who needeth hope," said Sigurd, "when the heart of the Volsungs turns to the Glittering Heath and the house of the serpent? I shall slay the foe of the Gods, as thou didst bid me, and then with the gold and its curse shalt thou be left alone."

"O child," said the King of the Dwarf Kind, "when the last day comes and 'tis the end even of the Gods, shalt thou praise thy hope and the Gods that made this world?"

"Foe of the Gods," said Sigurd, "now thou wouldst hide the evil thing, and the curse that is greater than thou, lest death should overtake thee. It is me, it is me thou fearest, if indeed I know thy thought; yea me, who would light up all good and evil with the glare of the sword."

And Sigurd sprang aloft to the saddle as he spake these words, and the Wrath burned in its sheath by his side. The sun rose and the grey pass in the mountains was filled with the living light, and Regin turned from the glory with eyes that were blinded and dazed. But Sigurd, seated on Greyfell, gleamed in the light, and he spake in a great voice:

"O Regin, in good sooth, I have hearkened not nor heeded thy words of fear and of foreboding. Thou hast told thy tale and thy longing and to that I hearkened well. The deed shall be done tomorrow; let it lead thee up to Heaven, or let it lead thee down to Hell. Thou shalt have the measureless gold; with the blood and the might of thy brother thou shalt sate thy hunger, and this deed shall be mine and thine. But take heed for what followeth after! Let us each do after his kind! And for me, I shall do the deeds of men; to them shall I give my life days, and to the Gods my glory to keep."

Then Sigurd shook the bridle reins of Greyfell and rode forth from the mountain pass and took his way to the westward. And Regin, little and dark, followed after. And now Regin forgot his fears and thought only of the gold that should be his. So they journeyed on and on, between high mountain walls, past dark fathomless lakes that held no fish, nor any sign of life. So they kept riding to the westward and the mountains were grown huge and their peaks reached to the very heavens. They rode through the noontide, and the sun grew low, nor even then did they tarry though the world was dark about them. On and on they rode, each man alone, through the night. And though the stars and the moon grew pale, no change came over the darkness, and no streak of dawn lit the sky. In the blackness Sigurd felt for the walls of the pass, but though he rode first to one side and then the other, he found no wall before him. But lo, at last there came a glimmer in the sky, and the light grew, and a faint dawn came to the world. And Sigurd strained his eyes and all about him he saw a deserted land, barren and changeless as far as his eye could reach. Then his heart leapt up within him, for he knew that his journey was o'er, and here before him lay the first of the Glittering Heath. He drew the bridle and leapt down from Greyfell, and the Wrath burned in its sheath by his side, and on foot he wended his way through the grey light to meet the foe of the Gods.

Sigurd saw nought of Regin, nor did he take any heed of him. He strode across the desert heath and Greyfell paced behind him. As he wended his way in that silence a grey thing glimmered before him and became a mighty man, one-eyed and seeming ancient, and clad in cloud-grey raiment. A friendly man and glorious, and his face was smiling glad as he spake to Sigurd in a voice deep as the wind of winter:

"Hail, Sigurd! Give me thy greeting ere thou wendest thy ways alone!"

And Sigurd answered: "Hail! I greet thee, my friend and my fathers' friend."

"And whither," said the elder, "goest thou with the steed and the ancient sword?"

"To the house of the serpent, and the greedy king of the gold," said Sigurd.

"And wilt thou smite him, O Sigurd?" quoth the ancient grey-clad one.

"Yea, I shall smite," said the Volsung, "unless the Gods be against me."

"And how," said the elder, "shalt thou smite, so that thou thyself be not devoured?"

"Thou hast praised this sword," said Sigurd, "and the sword shall find a way."

"Be learned of me," said the Wise One, "for I was the first of thy folk."

And Sigurd answered: "I shall obey thy bidding, and for thee I shall do the deed."

Then spake the Wise One: "Thus shalt thou do when thou wendest again on thy way. Thou shalt come to a path, a road in this desert place that is smooth and deep and hollow. The rains have not made it, nor hath any wild wind worn that furrow, for it is Fafnir's track whereby he wends to the water and the ancient pool when he is athirst in the dawning. There remember the greatness of thy fathers, and bare thy sword, and dig a pit in that highway. Lie thou in it, O Sigurd, and be as dead for a season, and when the worm passeth over thee, then shalt thou thrust him through."

Said Sigurd: "I shall obey thy bidding, and for thee shall I do the deed. For I love thee, thou friend of my fathers, and wise heart of the holy folk."

So spake the son of Sigmund, but lo, no man was near. So Sigurd went on his way till he came to the path of Fafnir, and it was a mighty track. And Sigurd drew forth his Wrath and dug the pit as he had been told, and lay therein. Now the worm came on his way, and afar off Sigurd could hear him roaring, as he dragged him over the earth. And the roaring grew as he came nearer, and he snorted forth venom before him. Sigurd trembled not nor was afraid, but lay waiting in his path. Then the dark rolled over Sigurd and the blackness covered him, and he thought on the glory of his fathers, and gathered his strength and with a mighty upward thrust, drove his sword through the heart of the serpent. Then he leapt from the pit and the rushing river of blood.

But there lay Fafnir wounded with the death stroke, and the folds of the serpent lay huddled on the plain. And forth from the Face of Terror came the sound of speech:

"Child, who art thou that hast smitten me? And whence is thy birth?"

"I am called the Wild Thing Glorious, and alone I wend on the earth," answered Sigurd.

And Fafnir spake again: "Fierce child, and who was thy father?"

Quoth Sigurd: "Am I like to the sons of men folk that my father I should know?"

"Wert thou born of a nameless wonder?" asked Fafnir. "Come, speak me the truth on this, my death day."

"I am Sigurd the Volsung, the son of Sigmund the King."

Said Fafnir: "What master hath taught thee of murder? Hast thou not heard how all men feared me?"

"I desired the deed, and the bright sword learned the way."

And Fafnir answered: "Thou hast done it, thou child of

Sigmund, but the gold and the red rings shall bring thee evil."

"But I shall cast them abroad," quoth Sigurd, "so that all men may gather again."

Said Fafnir: "Thou art great in thine anger, and the Norns thou heedest not."

Then Sigurd asked: "O Fafnir, speak to me of the Norns and the wisdom thou hast from ancient days."

Said Fafnir: "Few things wilt thou do after my counsel, but take heed that thou shalt be drowned if thou farest unwarily over the sea; so bide thou rather on the dry land, and wait the coming of the calm tide."

Sigurd cried: "O Fafnir, tell me of the Norns ere thou layest down thy life."

And Fafnir said: "Many there are—and who shall name them all?—and they rule the lives of men folk."

"O Fafnir, what of the isle, and what name hath it, where the Gods shall mingle the swords with Surt and the Sons of Flame?"

Said Fafnir: "Unshapen yet is that end and destruction of all things."

"What then shall endure, to tell the tale of the world, O Fafnir?"

"I know not," answered Fafnir, "but I know that this rattling gold and these red rings shall bring evil unto thee."

[147]

"Yet mine hand shall scatter the gold, and the earth shall gather it," spake Sigurd.

"Woe, woe," cried Fafnir, "in the days that are past the hoarded gold and the Helm of Aweing were mine. I overcame and was mighty, till I met thine hand, O Sigurd. And I fought and fell in the morning, and I die far off from the gold."

Then Sigurd leaned on his sword, and a dreadful cry went by on the wind, and Fafnir died. Then all sank into silence and Sigurd stood alone on the desert by the pool of Fafnir's blood and before him lay the serpent, grey and dead.

So Sigurd stood, and now was Greyfell beside him, and Regin came from afar. He came afoot over the desert, and when he stood before Sigurd he stared at him and at the Wrath yet bloody and unsheathed, and at the serpent lying dead at the feet of Sigurd. Then Regin lay on the ground and drank the blood of the serpent where it lay in a pool. And he cried:

"Now shall I be free from the yoke that binds my soul to a withered body; now shall I have again the wisdom and might of the dwarfs."

And Regin turned and saw how Sigurd wiped the blood from his sword, and how above him a flock of mountain eagles screamed in the sky. And his mood grew dark and he came to Sigurd and spake:

"Child, thou hast slain my brother."

"Yea," answered Sigurd, "the deed is mine and thine. But now our ways shall go asunder."

But Regin crouched before him and spake: "Fare on to the murder of men and the deeds of thy kindred. Surely of thee and of them the tale shall be speedily told. Thou hast slain thy master's brother, and what wouldst thou say thereto if thou wert judged for it?"

Then spake Sigurd as before: "The deed is mine and thine. And now our ways shall sunder, and into the world will I pass."

But Regin darkened before him and grew exceeding grim: "Thou hast slain my brother, and wherewith wilt thou atone?"

"Stand up, O Master," cried Sigurd, "and take the wealth I have won for thee, ere we go our ways. I have toiled and thou hast desired, and the treasure is surely near, and thou hast the wisdom to find it."

But Regin cried to Sigurd: "Thou hast slain my brother."

"Take thou the gold," quoth Sigurd, "for the ransom of my head."

Again Regin cried: "Thou hast slain my brother, and today shalt thou be my cook boy and this heath my cooking hall."

And Regin crept to the coils of the serpent and drew a glaive from his side and cut the heart from Fafnir. Overhead the flock of wild eagles circled about. Then Regin spake to Sigurd:

"Wilt thou be free of this slaying? Then build thou a fire

and roast the heart for me, that I may eat it and live, and be thy master and more, for therein was might and wisdom. Or else, depart on thy ways afraid from the Glittering Heath."

Then Regin lay on the ground and slept, but his sword lay bare by his side with his hand on the hilt. He seemed a fearful thing as he lay and dreamed of the power that should be his.

So Sigurd took the heart. He found waste wood on the heath, and he built a hearth of stones and kindled a fire, and he sat before it and sang as he roasted the heart. The eagles flew low about him, but he little heeded their cries. After the heart had roasted for a space, Sigurd reached his hand to see if the cooking were enough. But the blood and fat seethed forth and scalded Sigurd's finger and he put it quick in his mouth to quench the smart. And thus he tasted the flesh of the serpent and the blood of Fafnir's heart. Then there came a change upon him, for he knew the speech of fowl, and grew as wise in the ways of the beast kind as were the dwarfs of old.

And he knit his brows and hearkened and began to understand the cries of the eagles that circled above. And wrath rose in his heart for he saw the net of evil and death that Regin sought to draw about him. For the eagles cried out a warning to Sigurd that Regin would wake from his sleep all-powerful and cunning with the ancient craft of the dwarf kind and that he would destroy Sigurd. Thus, from the beginning, had he planned. For the eagles cried:

"He hath reared up a king for the slaying, that he alone might live."

With the eagles crying about him, Sigurd rose swiftly and the Wrath gleamed in his hand. Regin lay in sleep, but his eyes glared wide-open and his hand was on his sword. And his lips smiled as he slept, for he dreamt that Sigurd was no more and that he at last was master of the world. But Sigurd saw the evil in Regin's heart and cried aloud in his wrath:

"Thou wouldst betray me and keep me here for my destruction, that my death might serve thy need. It is for this thou feared me and my sword. Lo then, here is the sword and the stroke! Let the Norns judge betwixt us! But I will not die the death of a tame thing, nor yield my hope to thee!"

Then the Wrath of Sigurd flashed thin and white and the head of Regin was severed from his body. And there in that desert place lay Regin, lifeless by the side of his brother, Fafnir the Serpent. But Sigurd cried in triumph:

"The blind heart of the dwarf kind shall not rule the world. Dead are the foes of the Gods!"

Then Sigurd himself ate of the Heart of Fafnir and grew wise in the ancient wisdom of the dwarf kind. Then he leapt aback of Greyfell and rode forth in search of the treasure of Andvari. Sigurd followed the track of Fafnir, and still the eagles flew above him, until at length he reached the dwelling of the serpent. It was builded of unwrought iron and it went high to

[151]

the heavens and reached deep into the earth, and there was nought within it save the heaped-up piles of gold.

Sigurd entered and beheld the wealth of Andvari's treasure. There was coin of ancient cities and war gear and spoil from the battle field; there was rich ore from the depths of the earth where none but the dwarfs had mined; and tawny gold from the sands of rivers no man had discovered. And in the midst of all these riches glittered the Helm of Aweing and beside it the War Coat of Gold, the like of which there was not anywhere in the heavens or the earth. Sigurd beheld, moreover, Andvari's Ring of Gain, which Loki had so coveted. Then laughed the son of Sigmund and set the ring on his hand. Then he donned the Helm of Aweing and its fellow, the War Coat of Gold. Then he labored to bring forth that treasure and he toiled and loaded Greyfell, though it seemed more than one horse might bear. And as Sigurd went about the work the eagles sang above him:

"Bind the red rings, O Sigurd! let the gold shine free and clear!
  For what hath the son of the Volsungs the ancient Curse to fear?"

"Bind the red rings, O Sigurd! for thy tale is well begun,
  And the world shall be good and gladdened by the Gold lit up by the
      sun."

"Bind the red rings, O Sigurd! and gladden all thine heart!
  For the world shall make thee merry ere thou and she depart."

"Bind the red rings, O Sigurd! for the ways go green below,
Go green to the dwelling of Kings, and the halls that the Queen-folk
know."

"Bind the red rings, O Sigurd! for what is there bides by the way,
Save the joy of folk to awaken, and the dawn of the merry day?"

"Bind the red rings, O Sigurd! for the strife awaits thine hand,
And a plenteous war-field's reaping, and the praise of many a land."

"Bind the red rings, O Sigurd! But how shall storehouse hold
That glory of thy winning and the tidings to be told?"

Now when the steed was fully laden it was well on in the
night, and the stars shone. Then Sigurd took Greyfell's reins
and turned toward the wall of the mountains, for he deemed that
the way from the Glittering Heath lay hence. But Greyfell would
move not a whit for aught that Sigurd might do. Then Sigurd
pondered a space, till he knew the will of Greyfell, and then, clad
all in his war gear, he leapt into the saddle; and with a proud and
mirthful toss of his head Greyfell sprang unspurred over the
desert plain. Light and swift he went and breasted the wall of
the mountains and climbed the summit. And the Glittering
Heath, that dread place where the Serpent had so long held
sway, was left behind.

How Sigurd awakes Brynhild upon Hindfell

When Sigurd had passed beyond the Glittering Heath he found himself in a place of great crags and mountains. Greyfell went swift and light and Sigurd turned somewhat to the southward, for he longed to hear again the speech of men and to be with his own kind. But the desert still endured and he had ridden a long road when, early on a morning, he saw before him a mighty mountain. The clouds about its top were lit with flame as though a great torch burned there. Sigurd turned toward the mountain, for from thence he deemed that he might look over the world and see which way was best to take.

So he rode higher and higher, and a strange light shone about him from those flame-lit clouds on the mountain's crest. Toward noon the clouds grew darker and settled thickly, hiding the top of the mountain from Sigurd's sight, but he kept riding ever higher and higher toward it. In the late afternoon the winds blew up and the clouds were cleared away and again Sigurd saw the mountain. But the light that had seemed a torch from afar off was now a blazing river of fire, and the mountain was black above it and below it, and the head of Hindfell rose like an island in the sunset sky.

Night fell, but yet Sigurd rode on and on, and had no thought of rest, for he longed to climb that mighty rock and look forth over the world. As he came among the foot-hills he could see the light no more, but the stars were lovely and gleaming above him. He rode on through a dark pass in the mountain till the stars were dimmed and the world grew cold with the dawn. Then afar off he beheld a breach in the rock wall and forth from it poured a flood of light. Swiftly Sigurd rode thither and found the place. He drew up Greyfell and gazed in wonder on the marvel before him. For lo, the side of Hindfell was enwrapped by a fervent blaze and there was nought betwixt earth and heaven save a shifting world of flame. Sigurd cried to Greyfell and they hastened up and nearer, until he drew rein in the dawning on the steep side of Hindfell. But Sigurd heeded not the dawning, for before him the flames wove a great wavering wall. No wind could drive it back, nor could rain drench it, nor was there any opening or pause in it for the wayfarer to pass through. A mammoth wall of fire, it flamed before Sigurd. Sigurd trembled not, but smiled as the breath of it lifted up his hair, and his eyes shone bright with its image and his coat of mail gleamed white and fair. In his war helm the heavens and the waning stars behind him were reflected. But Greyfell stretched his neck to snuff at the flame wall and his cloudy flanks heaved. In the great light the gold of Andvari heaped upon the steed was waxen wan and pale.

Then turned Sigurd in his saddle and drew the girths tighter and shifted the hilt of his Wrath. Gathering up the reins, he cried aloud to Greyfell and rode straight at the wildfire's heart. But the flame wall wavered before him and parted and rose o'er his head, roaring wild above him. But he rode through its roaring as a warrior rides through a field of waving rye. The white flame licked his raiment and swept through Greyfell's mane. It covered Sigurd's hands and the hilt of his sword and wound about his helmet and his hair. But the fire hurt him not, neither was his raiment marred nor his war gear dimmed. Then of a sudden the flames failed and faded and darkened, and a heavy murkiness spread over the earth. Sigurd rode further till all was calm about him; then he turned his eyes backward. The side of Hindfell blazed no longer, but behind him on the scorched earth lay a ring of pale slaked ashes. And beyond it the waste world of crags and mountains lay hushed and grey in the early dawn.

Then before him Sigurd saw a Shield-burg, a wall of many shields wrought clear without a flaw. Silver shields gleamed beside those of gold and ruddy shields beside the white, and all were carved and blazoned brightly. The wall rose high to the heavens and o'er the topmost shield rim there hung, like a banner, a glorious golden buckler. It swayed in the morning breeze and rang against the staff that held it.

Sigurd leapt down from Greyfell and stood before the wall. It rose above him as though 'twere the very dwelling of the Gods and he looked but little beneath it. He drew not his sword from its scabbard as he wended his way round the rampart. All was silent; 'twas only the wind and Sigurd that wakened any sound. Then lo, he came to the gate, and its doors were open wide. No warder withstood his way and no earls guarded the threshold. Sigurd stood a while and marveled at such strangeness. Then his Wrath gleamed bare in his hand as he wended his way inward, for he doubted some guile of the Gods, or some dwarf king's snare, or perchance a mock of the giant people that should fade before his eyes. But he took his way in and he saw the wall of shields, with the ruddy by the white and the silver by the gold, but within that wall no work of man was set. There was nought but the utmost head of Hindfell rising high. Then, as Sigurd gazed, he beheld below in the very midmost a giant-fashioned mound that was builded as high as the topmost rim of the shield wall. And there, on that mound of the giants, with nought but the wilderness about, a pale grey image lay and gleamed in the early morn.

So there was Sigurd alone in that desert of wonder; and he went forward with the Sword of the Branstock high in his hand.

He set his face toward the earth mound and beheld the image, with the dawn growing light about it; and lo, he saw 'twas the shape of a man set forth in that desert place on the tower top of the world. So Sigurd climbed the mound to see if the man were living or dead, and who it was that lay there: some king of the days forgotten, or mayhap the frame of a God, or e'en some glorious heart beloved laid far from earthly strife. He stood over the body and saw that it was shapen fair and clad from head to foot-sole in pale grey-glittering mail as closely wrought as though it were grown to the flesh. A war helm, girt with a golden crown, hid the face from view. Sigurd stooped and knelt beside the figure, and he felt a breath as sweet as a summer wind come forth from the sleeping one. Then spake Sigurd to himself that he would look on the face and see whether it bore him love or hate and who it might be that so strangely rested here. So he drew the helm from the head, and lo, Sigurd beheld the snow-white brow, and the smooth unfurrowed cheeks, and the lightly breathing lips of a woman. A woman fair beyond all dreaming. And Sigurd looked, and he loved her sore, and longed to move her spirit and waken her heart to the world.

Gently he touched her and spake softly: "Awake! I am Sigurd." But she moved not.

Then looked Sigurd on the bare blade beside him. The pale blue edges burned brightly as the sun began to rise. The rims of the Shield-burg glittered and the east grew exceeding clear. Sigurd took the Sword of the Branstock and set the edge to the dwarf-wrought coat of mail where the ring-knit collar constrained the woman's throat. The sharp Wrath bit and rended the rings, and lo, white linen gleamed softly beneath the armor. Sigurd drove the blue steel onward through the coat and the skirt of mail, till nought but the rippling linen was wrapping her about. Then he deemed her breath came quicker, and he turned the Wrath and cut down either sleeve. Her arms lay white in her raiment and glorious sun-bright hair fell shining across her shoulders.

Then a flush came over her visage, a sigh stirred her breast, her eyelids quivered and opened, and slowly she awakened. Wide-eyed she gazed on the dawning, too glad to change or smile; nor did she speak, and moved but little. Motionless beside her Sigurd knelt, waiting her first words, while the soft waves of the daylight sped over the starless heavens. The gleaming rims of the Shield-burg grew bright and yet brighter in the rising sun, and the thin moon hung her horns dead-white in the golden glow.

Then she turned and gazed on Sigurd and her eyes met the Volsung's eyes, and mighty and measureless within him now swelled the tide of his love. Their longing met and mingled, and he knew in his heart that she loved, as she spake softly to him:

"O, what is the thing so mighty that hath torn my weary sleep?"

Sigurd answered: "The hand of Sigurd and the Sword of Sigmund's son, and the heart that the Volsungs fashioned have done this deed for thee."

But she said: "Where then is Odin who hath laid me here? O, long is the grief of the world, and mankind's tangled woe!"

"Odin dwelleth above," said Sigurd, "but I dwell on the earth. And I came from the Glittering Heath to ride the waves of thy fire."

Even as he spake the sun rose upward and lightened all the earth, and the light flashed back to the heavens from the glorious gleaming shields. The twain uprose together, and as the risen sun bathed them in the light of the new day, she lifted her arms with palms outspread and cried:

"All hail, O Day and thy Sons, and thy kin of the coloured things!
  Hail, following Night, and thy Daughter that leadeth thy wavering
      wings!
  Look down with unangry eyes on us today alive,
  And give us the hearts victorious, and the gain for which we strive!
  All hail, ye Lords of God-home, and ye Queens of the House of Gold!
  Hail, thou dear Earth that bearest, and thou Wealth of field and fold!
  Give us, your noble children, the glory of wisdom and speech,
  And the hearts and the hands of healing, and the mouths and the
      hands that teach!"

They turned then and embraced, and gladness and rejoicing filled their hearts. Spake Sigurd:

"Thou art the fairest of the earth, and the wisest of the wise; O who art thou? I am Sigurd, e'en as I told thee. I have slain the Serpent Fafnir and gotten the ancient gold. Great indeed were the gift of my days if I should gain thy love and we twain, through all of life, should never part. O who art thou that lovest, thou who art fairest of all things born? And what meaneth thy lonely slumber here?"

Said she: "I am she that loveth. I was born of earthly folk, but long ago Allfather took me from the home of the kings and he called me the Victory Wafter. I came and went and at Odin's will chose the victor on the battle field, and the slain for his war host; and my days were glorious and good. But the thoughts of my heart overcame me and pride in my wisdom and power, and I deemed that I alone could choose the slain, and scorned the will of Allfather. For that came my punishment. Allfather decreed that I should return again among men, to be one of them. But I cried: 'If I must live and wed in the world, and gather grief on the earth, then the fearless heart shall I wed. E'en there shall I fashion a tale brave and fair, that shall give hope to the Earth.'

"Allfather smiled somewhat, but he spake: 'So let it be! Still thy doom abideth. Fare forth, and forget and be weary 'neath the Sting of the Sleepful Thorn, and long shall the time pass over e'er the day of thy waking come.'

"So I came to the head of Hindfell and there the sleep thorn pierced me and the slumber fell on me, from which none might wake me save him who would not turn back from the waving flames of the wild fire. And that is the tale. Now I am she that loveth; and the day is near when I, who have ridden the sea realm and the regions of the land and dwelt in the measureless mountains, shall live once more in the house of my fathers. There shall the days be joyous. Lo now, I look on thine heart and behold thine inmost will and know that thou wouldst have me tell thee of the days that shall be ours. But restrain thy desire, as thou restrainest the steed in the beginning of the battle, lest toward its ending his limbs grow weary and fail thee. Ask me not of the future, lest thou ask of the thing thou shouldst not and the thing 'twere better not to know.

"Know thou, most mighty of men, that the Norns shall order all things, and yet without thy helping their will cannot come to pass. 'Tis strange, and the fool and the blind believe it not, but I know; I have seen it writ in the heavens. The evil days of the world are born of the malice and cowardice of men, but the fair days of the earth, when the sun shines and good is brought forth, they are fashioned of daring deeds and the eager hearts of love. So loosen thy sword in the scabbard and settle thy war helm firm, for men betrayed are mighty and great are the wrongfully dead.

"Wilt thou repent the deeds that thou dost? Then 'twere better not to have been born. Wilt thou exalt thy deeds? Then thy fame shall pass thee by. Do thou the deed and abide it, and look steadfastly upon the days as they pass.

"Love thou the Gods, but be not their thrall and their bondsman, for thou wert born for their very friend. Few things are hidden from the Gods and they know the hearts of men."

Then spake the maiden: "I have spoken these words, beloved, but 'tis thy heart and mine were speaking."

Again spake the son of Sigmund: "Fairest, and most of worth, thou knowest the ways of man folk. Then speak yet more of wisdom; for meseems it is most meet that my soul be shapen to thy soul."

She took his hand and there on the side of Hindfell their glad eyes looked and loved. And she told of the hidden matters whereby the world is moved: she told of the framing of all things, the houses of the heaven, the star worlds' courses, and how the winds be driven. She told of the Norns and their names, and the fate that abideth the earth. She told of the ways of the king folk, of the love of women, of the fall of mighty houses, of the friend that falters and turns, and the grief that endureth for long.

"Aye," she spake, "but man shall bear and forbear, and be master of all that is; man shall measure it all, the wrath, and the grief, and the bliss.

"I sought Wisdom and prayed her to come for my teaching; but 'tis only Allfather who sees her light. Yet is each man wise to do bravely and well that thing that the Gods have given him to do. Wise is the sower that sows, and wise is the reaper that reaps, and wise shalt thou be to deliver. And lo, a glorious tale shall be told of thee, of thy sword and the wakening fire.

"Hark now, how Greyfell neighs and the gold of Fafnir gleams upon him. Green go the roads to the children of men and the deeds that thou shalt do. Come now, O Sigurd, for now is the high noon come and the sun hangs over Hindfell and looks on the homes of the earth folk. Thy soul is great within thee and glorious are thine eyes. And I long that we twain may see men's dwellings and the house where we shall dwell, the place of our life's beginning."

So they climbed the burg of Hindfell. Hand in hand they fared till all about and above them was nought but the sunlit air. Far away beneath lay the kingdoms of the earth and the place of men folk's dwellings: the rich and plenteous acres, the silver ocean's hem, and the woodland wastes and the mountains.

Then spake the Victory Wafter: "O Sigurd, as a God thou beholdest thine heritage. And where on the wings of thy hope is thy spirit born? But now I bid thee pause and look on the land twixt the wood and the silver sea; there near the swirling river is the house where I was born. Mine earthly sister and the king that she hath wed dwell there. There in days gone by I woke on a golden bed, and noon by noon I wandered and plucked the blossoming flowers, and eve by eve I tarried amid the speech and the lays of kings. Brynhild was I called in the days ere my father died. That is the land of Lymdale betwixt the woodland and the sea."

"I shall seek thee there," said Sigurd, "when the spring is come, ere we wend the world together in the season of the sun."

"I shall bide thee there," said Brynhild.

Then from his hand Sigurd drew Andvari's ancient gold. There was nought but the sky above them as together they held the ring, the shapen ancient token that hath no change nor end.

Then cried Sigurd: "O Brynhild, now hearken while I swear that the sun shall die in the heavens and the day no more be fair, if I seek thee not in Lymdale in the house that fostered thee!"

And Brynhild cried: "O Sigurd, Sigurd, now hearken while I swear that the day shall die for ever and the sun to blackness wear ere I forget thee, Sigurd, as I wait in the land of Lymdale in the house that fostered me!"

Then Sigurd set the ring on Brynhild's finger and their arms were about each other and their hearts were full and glad. The day grew old about them and eve and the sunset came. The twilight changed and died and the stars shone forth on the world, ere they turned and went the roads that go green to the dwellings of men.

Far away beneath lay the silver ocean's hem.

Such are the tales that are told of Volsung, and of Sigmund his son, and of
Sigurd, who was mightiest of them all.
More befell Sigurd in the days that were
to come, both of grief and of joy, but
these were the deeds of his youth.